A Year of Jewish Stories

"A Book Is a Friend You
Can Return to Again and Again"

⁂

In loving memory of Larissa Lippe
Whose lifelong dedication
to young readers
Is memorialized by her family.

A Year of
JEWISH STORIES

52 Tales for Children and Their Families

GRACE RAGUES MAISEL
and SAMANTHA SHUBERT

Illustrated by
TAMMY L. KEISER

UAHC Press · New York, New York

To my mother, Olga Safadie Ragues, who taught me to read,
to my father, Alberto Esteban Ragues, z"l,
who taught me to love books,
to my children, Remy, Zoe, Skye, and Willow,
to whom I pass along those gifts,
and to my husband, Louis, for making it possible.

—G.R.M.

To Rebecca and Hannah, whose stories are my favorites.

—S.S.

Acknowledgments

We would like to thank Lynn Feinman and Steven W. Siegel of the
92nd Street Y's Buttenwieser Library for their invaluable assistance
and encouragement. Ilana Abend-David of the Park Avenue Synagogue
Library gave generously of her time and research advice. We are especially
grateful to Rabbi Hara Person, who edited this book with wisdom, care,
and a sense of humor. We would also like to thank everyone else at the
UAHC Press who lent their expertise to this book, including Ken Gesser,
Joel Eglash, Liane Broido, and Debra Hirsch Corman.

Library of Congress Cataloging-in-Publication Data

A year of Jewish stories: 52 tales for children and their families/retold
by Grace Ragues Maisel and Samantha Shubert; illustrated by Tammy Keiser.
    p. cm.
  Includes bibliographical references and index.
  ISBN 0-8074-0895-6 (hardcover:alk. paper)
   1. Legends, Jewish. 2. Fasts and feasts—Judaism. 2. Jews—Folklore. I. Maisel,
Grace Ragues. II. Shubert, Samantha. III. Keiser, Tammy.

BM530.Y43 2003
296.1'40521—dc   212003047342

Contents

Contents

Contents

Introduction

As parents of small children, we are confronted daily with many small but important decisions. Whether studying lists of ingredients or choosing a day camp, we are really asking ourselves one question: "What do I want to give my children?" We all want to give them a healthy, happy environment and a strong sense of who they are. For Jews, whether completely secular or traditionally observant, the question that naturally follows is: "How can I help my children grow up happy to be Jewish?"

Given the wide range of religious observance, it's impossible to imagine a single defining moment that would inspire children to grow into adulthood with pride in their heritage. The process of building a child's Jewish identity begins with the baby steps of simple explanations, loving memories, and family traditions. But where do you start? How do you teach a love of Judaism to the younger child? If your background is secular, how do you create memories where there are none? How do you explore Jewish values together without coming across as preachy?

The answer is—as it probably has always been—through the magic of storytelling.

Following the Jewish calendar, we have chosen stories from the Bible, Talmud, midrash, and folklore for each week of the year. There are also plenty of stories for the weeks in between holidays. While this book is firmly grounded in the classics, its sensibility is a modern one. If you're looking for a story to complement a holiday, you'll find one in the table of contents. If you want to highlight a specific value or virtue, let the Topic Index in the back guide your search. If you just want to immerse yourselves in the world of our heritage, jump right in, find an appealing story, and start a new weekly ritual of reading with your children.

We are offering you an easy and open invitation into the richness of Jewish life—the aroma of freshly baked challah, the warmth of a teacher's hug, the sound of the Red Sea parting. We want this invitation to be as welcoming as Abraham's tent, which is said to have been open on three sides and situated at a crossroads so as to accept as many guests as possible. We welcome parents and small children, non-Jewish friends and family, educators and school kids, camp counselors, rabbis, grandparents—anyone who thirsts and hungers for a Jewish identity.

B'ruchim habaim. Welcome.

❧ 1 ❧

The Angels Argue

God was putting some finishing touches on the world, and the angels, hovering nearby, were admiring all of the new creations.

"What's your favorite thing?" one angel asked another.

"Oh, I don't know," the second angel answered lazily. "It's all wonderful. But my favorite thing is probably that great big night light in the sky."

"I think God calls that the Moon," said the first angel. "Yes, it's pretty, but *my* favorite is that curved shape with all the colors in it. You know, the thing in the sky after a storm. I love the way the colors all blend into one another. And I love the way you can't really see its beginning or its end. It's called a . . . a . . ."

"I'm pretty sure its name is Rainbow," another angel interrupted. "Now, me, I love those little colorful plants that grow out of the ground. I love the way they start as seeds and then they grow and then they make more seeds, which grow into more of those plant things, which will make more seeds . . . and it will just keep going forever and ever."

"Flowers, those are called Flowers," God said. "Yes, all of this is good. There is only one thing still missing."

"Missing?" asked the angels in surprise. "What could be missing? The world is perfect." They flew to the base of God's throne, their wings flapping softly.

"What's missing," God said, "is *Man*."

The angels' wings began to flap a little harder.

"Man?" they all said at the same time. "What's Man?"

"Man is not a what," explained God. "Man is a who. Man is the whole reason I created the world. I'm glad you like the Moon. But it hardly matters to *you*

· 3 ·

whether it is day or night." God turned to another angel and said, "And the Rainbow is nice, but it doesn't matter to *you* whether it rains or not. It doesn't matter to *you* whether a seed grows or not. But all of this will matter to Man very much."

Now the angels no longer looked like children settling down for a bedtime story. They flitted back and forth, whispering to each other and looking rather upset.

Finally, one angel asked God defiantly, "This Man—why exactly do you need to create him?"

"I will give Man a soul and wisdom, so he can help me finish creating the world," said God. "His soul will enjoy all the splendor of the world. And his wisdom will bring fairness and justice to the world."

The Angel of Justice perked up immediately. "Oh, create Man then! Yes, by all means."

But the Angel of Peace looked worried. "If you give Man wisdom, he will think for himself, and thinking for yourself leads to arguing. Don't create Man! He'll only make war!"

The Angel of Forgiveness did not agree. "Let Man be created. Because of his good soul, he can choose to be kind and generous."

But the Angel of Truth spoke most harshly of all. "Give Man a choice, and he will probably choose to lie!"

While the angels were busy with their arguments, God went ahead and created Man.

God turned to the angels and said, "You are all very wise, but Man's wisdom will be even greater than yours. And tomorrow, I will show you how."

The following day, God arranged every kind of beast and bird and flower before the angels. God then asked the angels to name the creations, but they couldn't. They merely whispered and murmured together. Finally, they fell silent.

Then God called Man. At first, Man did not answer either. He was lost in thought, admiring the shape of a honeycomb and savoring the taste of the honey inside.

"He doesn't seem too bright to me," one angel whispered to another.

"Man!" God called. "*Man!*" Finally, Man looked up. "Tell me," said God, "what would you call these things?"

Without hesitation, Man put his face right up to the swarm of buzzing creatures. He studied their heavy, fuzzy bodies, and listened carefully to their humming. "Hmmm, hmmm," he mimicked, and then said, "Bees. Yes, they're called Bees."

God seemed happy with that answer, so Man walked a few paces further. He stared deeply into the eyes of another, much larger creature. He gently stroked its mane and, closing his eyes, hugged the animal close to his heart. Then he said confidently, "This is Horse."

Next, a furry, slobbering creature bounded up and knocked Man over. Man picked himself up, laughing, and patted the friendly animal. "This is Dog," he said. And Dog followed Man around for the rest of the day while he named every creature and tree and flower.

The angels watched, holding their breath, but God was very pleased. Finally, God asked, "And you, Man, what should we call you?"

"Call me Adam," he answered simply. "Because I was created from *adamah*, from the earth."

"Well done, Adam, well done," laughed God. "And now, because you've shown us how well you use your wisdom, I will create Woman to share the world with you." God turned to the angels and added, "Unless, of course, anyone has a problem with *that* idea?"

One angel asked nervously, "Will she be as smart as Man?"

"She will be at least as smart," answered God.

"Well, then, no problem here." And one by one, the angels lifted their wings. "Man, Woman, great idea," they whispered, soaring away, until all that could be heard was the gentle flutter of wings.

❖ 2 ❖

The Just-Right Prayer

I t was a busy night for the angels. On Erev Yom Kippur, it was their job to visit Jews all over the world to hear their prayers. And so, just as the sun was about to set, the angels flew off to every corner of the Earth.

One angel was especially pleased with his assignment, which would surely be the easiest: he was headed for a magnificent synagogue in a big town. How wonderful it would be to witness the service there on this night of nights! The prayers of the townspeople would be heartfelt, the white robes of the rabbi and cantor would shine, and the beauty of the songs would mix with tears of real repentance. No matter how difficult the past year had been, the angel knew he could count on this one night of perfect beauty.

The angel slipped in just as Kol Nidre began. As he expected, voices of the townspeople—some booming, some nearly whispering—rose in a symphony of prayer to God. He heard real sorrow in their voices as they remembered how they'd sometimes acted badly in the past year. And he heard real hope in their voices when they told God how sorry they were and how they would try to change in the year ahead. The angel leaned back against a wall, sighing with contentment. Yes, this assignment was truly a pleasure.

But, as the angel closed his eyes, a different sound caught his attention. Was it a prayer, or perhaps a song, or maybe just a thought? What was it? He didn't know, but it was the most beautiful sound he had ever heard! Where was it coming from? The angel rushed from person to person, listening closely. No, it wasn't coming from here. Or over here. He watched the faces of the people as they prayed. Everyone's head followed the words of the prayer book, and their lips mouthed the words from its pages. But what he heard was something different.

God would certainly want to know about this sound, and the angel *had* to find it. He followed the sound as it led him outside. His eyes scanned the forest at the edge of the town. In the distance, he could just make out the low lights from a little house tucked in between the trees. The angel followed that beautiful sound to the door of the house, and he leaned against it to hear better.

Now, he could make out the sound quite clearly. It was the voice of a girl singing. He heard: "*Sh-maaaaaaaaaaaaa.*" There was a long pause. Then: "*Yis-ra-ellllll.*"

A different, lower, voice said, "Good! That's just right! Now you say, '*Adonai Eloheinu.*'"

There was a very long pause. Finally, the little voice said, "Grandpa, those words are too hard and too long. Why can't I just talk to God the way I want?"

"Because, sweetheart, you have to know the right words. And the *Sh'ma* is only the beginning! There are lots more prayers to learn after you get this one just right . . ."

"But I don't *want* to say it just right," the girl complained. "I'm going to say it my way."

"Oh, really?" said the deeper voice. "And what *is* your way?"

"I don't know. I'd probably say: 'Listen God, thanks. Thanks for everything. Thanks so much for my house, and Mom and Daddy and Grandpa. And I'm sorry, I'm so sorry . . . that my Grandpa is so stubborn! Just as stubborn as Mom, and she's almost as stubborn as me, and—"

The angel leaned forward, but he couldn't quite make out the next words. All he heard was both voices laughing. The sound of their laughter echoed against every tree in the forest. The leaves of the great cedars rustled like pages in an old *siddur.*

The angel straightened up. He had found what he was searching for, and off he flew to give his report.

There was a long line in front of him, but the angel waited patiently. Finally, it was his turn. God set down a very large book and asked, "So, was it nice? Which synagogue did you visit this year?"

The angel thought of the child's prayer and her laughter. And he answered, "Oh, yes, it was beautiful. But it wasn't exactly a synagogue. It was just a small house nestled among the cedars of Lebanon. There was a prayer, though. And it was beautiful, just beautiful."

❧ 3 ❧

So What?

Nothing made Rabbi Mordechai happier than starting each day in precisely the same way. First, he checked the alignment of his books and nudged the few that were out of place. Next, he would drop a coin into each of his *tzedakah* boxes in exactly the same order—the fund for widows, the fund for orphans, the fund for new books—*clink, clink, clonk*. Then, he'd kiss his children as they went off to school—oldest first and youngest last.

"So what if you don't kiss them in the right order? They'll all get kissed," his wife, Ruth, would say, sighing as he lined them up.

But Rabbi Mordechai always answered, "It matters—*to me*."

Rabbi Mordechai usually looked forward to his trips to the market. But today was the day before Sukkot, and each of the 2,590 steps from his house brought yet another worry. The roof of his family's sukkah—how would he cut all the branches exactly the same length? He would probably have to rearrange the children's decorations a few times. And—he would never say anything, of course—but the carrots in Ruth's tzimmes were always cut in different-size chunks and sliced every which way. . . . Rabbi Mordechai grimaced. He knew what she would say if he mentioned it. But it did matter, it *did!*

He tried to distract himself by thinking, instead, of what he *could* control. He was going to spend the next few hours, at least, poring over a cart laden with *lulavim* for Sukkot. He would pick the greenest *lulav* with the tightest, most beautifully arranged branches. He would make sure that the palm branch in the middle was perfectly straight and that the willow on one side was exactly the same height as the sweet-smelling myrtle on the other. And the *etrog* he would choose! Rabbi Mordechai began to walk more quickly just imagining it. He would handle each *etrog* with the gentlest touch, looking for the perfect one destined to be his own. It would have not a single mark on its bumpy yellow skin. And the sharp, lemony fragrance! He could smell it now. He could picture himself saying the blessing over the *lulav* in one hand and the *etrog* in the other. The shining faces of Ruth and the children—standing from tallest to smallest, naturally—would be gathered around in their cozy sukkah as he shook the *lulav* in all directions to show that God was everywhere. "Ah!" he murmured, dizzy with anticipation. "Just so! Just so!" And he burst into happy tears at this vision of perfection.

"Oh, Rabbi Mordechai," called a voice very close by, "I see that you are miserable, too!"

His beautiful dream popped into a million pieces. He was just about to answer that his tears were, on the contrary, from the highest joy, but the voice interrupted him again, this time crying, "Oh-ho-ho, what a pathetic wretch I am!"

At the side of the road sat Mina the Water Carrier, sniffling and whimpering. Her hair was disheveled, and her apron was filthy. By her side a skinny horse lay in the mud, along with the broken-down wagon it had been pulling.

"Oh, what will become of me without my poor horse?" the woman wept. "I made him work too hard, and now look, the poor thing!"

Rabbi Mordechai cleared his throat. Surely, he must offer her some comfort. "I'm sure it was not your fault," he began.

But Mina just covered her face with her apron and groaned into it. "Ooooh-ho-ho! Without him, how can I carry water to all my customers? I'm ruined!"

Rabbi Mordechai glanced back to the road. Only 100 paces more to the market—no, probably 110. "I'm sure everything will work out in the end," he offered weakly.

The woman rocked fiercely back and forth. "How will my poor children ever survive?" she wailed. "Now we have nothing! *Ooooooh*-ho-ho!"

Rabbi Mordechai knew what he had to do, but he hesitated for a moment before doing it. "Of course, I will give my holiday money to this poor woman," he thought. "But that means . . ." His imagination could go no further. Having no *lulav* and no *etrog* would mean a great, gaping hole in the middle of his perfect celebration.

"Look," he told Mina, thrusting all his coins into her apron pocket, "I-I-I just found this money. Maybe God meant for you to buy a new horse with it." And he ran off before the surprised woman could thank him. He was so upset that he didn't even remember to count his steps.

When Rabbi Mordechai got home, he walked round and round his family's sukkah with a distracted air. His oldest daughter grinned with pride as she showed off the roof branches, which were spaced just so. The chairs inside were lined up carefully. The children had even managed to use all the same colors for their decorations. It was the tidiest sukkah imaginable, but it did not cheer him.

Rabbi Mordechai followed the smell of cinnamon from Ruth's tzimmes and wandered into the kitchen. "Well," he finally said to her, "I'm sorry to have to say we won't have a *lulav* or *etrog* this year."

She stopped chopping an onion and looked at him with concern. "Mordechai, what happened?"

Rabbi Mordechai sighed heavily. "You know Mina the Water Carrier? Her horse died. I gave her our holiday money to buy a new horse. I know it was the right thing to do, but—"

"Of course it was the right thing," said his wife, nodding and returning to her chopping board. "So what if we can't have our own *lulav* and *etrog* this year? The poor horse. And poor Mina. . . ."

Rabbi Mordechai was on the verge of answering that it did matter. It mattered a lot! Sukkot is not Sukkot without an *etrog* to sniff and a *lulav* to wave! But then he realized how foolish his complaining would sound. And so, that night—despite a delicious dinner in the sukkah, despite much singing and dancing and clapping—the order of the holiday was upset, and Rabbi Mordechai was upset, too.

He slept so fitfully that his wife finally turned over and stared at him. "Mordechai, it bothers you, doesn't it? That we don't have a *lulav* or *etrog* to bless, I mean," Ruth said. He merely grunted his agreement. "I can see you won't feel better until you do," she sighed, getting out of bed. "So let's go."

"Let's go where?" Rabbi Mordechai said, pushing his face back into the pillow.

"Come on." She tossed her shawl over one shoulder, grabbed his arm, and pulled him to his feet. He glanced around in bewilderment as they lurched out the front door and into the chilly air. Where were they going? Ruth would never steal a *lulav*, would she? Were they going to borrow someone else's? All this, just to make him feel better?

Finally, they stopped at the edge of a boggy pasture. Through the early-morning haze, they could barely make out Mina's shack. It looked just as shabby

as the little barn next to it. A horse—it must be the new one Mina had bought with his money—poked its nose out the door in curiosity and ambled over to the fence.

"Ruth, dear, what are we doing here?" said Rabbi Mordechai.

His wife waited until the horse nuzzled her hand and said quietly, "Blessed is God, who made wonderful things like this in the world." She patted the horse on the nose and turned to her husband. "There! Now your blessing is said."

"Wait a minute, that's not right," Rabbi Mordechai said, wrinkling up his nose at the mistake. "That's the blessing for seeing something special."

"So what?" said Ruth, holding out one of her misshapen carrot chunks for the horse to nibble on. "A million other people may be blessing their *lulavim* this week to show that God is everywhere, but we are doing the same thing. The only reason this horse is standing here is that you gave *tzedakah*. You gave your money to help make someone else's life better. If *that* doesn't show that God is everywhere, I don't know what does."

Rabbi Mordechai had no answer. He was too busy counting all the times his wife had been right. That was forty-three times, just this week—or was it forty-four? Oh, he thought, grabbing Ruth's hand and squeezing it happily, what does it matter?

❖ 4 ❖

The Bear Hug

A shiny rock, a dull coin, a half-eaten bit of candy, and some wilted wild-flowers—these were the treasures Aaron had spread out in front of him. He knew it was time to go home for lunch, but still he sat on his favorite rock, fingering his discoveries and watching the anthill in front of him.

It was Thursday, and every Thursday was the same: His mother would pull him onto her lap to try to teach him the alphabet. He would wiggle away and run back to his ant friends and his wildflowers. He would stay away too long. His mother would be worried, then angry. And, like clockwork, he would bring her a bouquet for the Shabbat table, and everything would be smoothed over again. Until next week.

So Aaron continued watching his colony of ants. Who cares about *alef* or *bet?* he thought indignantly. Ants can't read or write, and they don't seem to mind a bit. They're all busy with their work, like me. They can't be bothered with study-ing, and neither can I! He carefully unwrapped his candy and sucked on it very slowly, to make it last as long as possible. He was still hungry, though, and he knew he'd have to go home soon. But how could he, when Mama would have that look on her face and that book next to his plate?

That's the way it had been last week: "Don't you want to learn how to write your name, sweetie?" Mama had asked him at lunchtime.

"What for?" he said.

"If you study enough, maybe someday you can become a great scholar, like Papa!"

"If he's such a great scholar, why does he still need to study?" said Aaron.

"When *I* grow up, I want to make lots of money and have great adventures. I won't have time to sit around reading books."

And the week before, Mama had asked him, "Aaron, love, do you want to know who you were named after?"

"I know who I was named after—Uncle Aaron, your brother!"

"No, I mean from the Bible. Don't you want to know who the first Aaron was and what he did? There are some wonderful stories. . . ." She waved her paper and pencil under his nose like a plate of freshly baked cookies, but he didn't bite.

"Then you can tell them to me at bedtime, Mama. I'll be back soon. . . ."

And so it had gone for months—Aaron running off, Mama pleading, and time passing.

But when Aaron returned home today, he knew something was different. Mama stood outside their door, waiting for him, smiling a smile that was not entirely happy.

Sitting at the table was none other than the Great Rebbe. Aaron had seen him many times before. He knew that rumbling voice well. He had memorized that stern look. And now, here was the Great Rebbe himself, glaring at him, his beard tucked into the collar of his dark suit.

"I'll take care of this," the Great Rebbe was saying. His voice seemed even lower and more gruff than Aaron remembered it. "Leave the boy to me," he growled. "Just give me a minute with him, and you'll see!"

Aaron turned to run, but Mama was standing in his way. She shook her head slowly, as if to say, "No running away, not this time." There was no choice, then. Aaron turned, drew himself up, and faced his enemy.

"*Nu?* Say something, boy," the Great Rebbe said. "Do you know why I'm here?"

Aaron shook his head, but he did know, of course. Because he didn't want to study, he knew he was probably in for scolding, yelling, maybe even spanking. He set his mouth in a flat line and narrowed his eyes, ready for anything.

"I'm here to teach you Torah," the Great Rebbe said loudly. Then, without another word, he gathered Aaron to his chest and hugged him.

At first, Aaron felt nothing but relief; there was no punishment, after all! With a sigh, Aaron allowed his head to fall onto the Great Rebbe's shoulder, where he could smell the dust of books and the wool of the old man's coat.

The Great Rebbe did not relax his grip. Aaron was feeling so comfortable,

though, in that bear hug, that he had no thought of pulling away. His mother stood nodding and smiling in the corner of the room. Against the bulk of the thick coat, it was very quiet. When Aaron sighed again, he was surprised to breathe in the sweet smell of lavender.

As he closed his eyes, images of Hebrew letters began to dance in his mind like flickering flames. Letters came together, and the flames grew brighter and brighter, filling Aaron with warmth.

Finally, the Great Rebbe released him. "There, Aaron, that's your first lesson in Torah," he said. "Would you like to continue?"

"That was a lesson?" the boy stammered. "How was that a lesson?" He could still feel the imprint of the Great Rebbe's coat against his cheek.

"That's the *only* lesson," said the old man. His voice no longer seemed like a growl, just deep. "Love. How to love yourself, by living a good life. How to love others, by treating them the way you'd like to be treated. How to love the world that God made for us. Love is what makes our work different, and more important, than the work of your ants."

Aaron's mouth fell open. How could the Great Rebbe possibly know about the ants?

"I know about the candy and the wildflowers, too," the old man added. "I was a boy once, you know," he said, brushing some dirt and bits of grass from Aaron's shirt. He plucked a smashed flower bud from one of the boy's buttonholes and placed it carefully in his own hatband, where there was already a tiny stalk of lavender.

"So," the Great Rebbe told Aaron's mother, "it's all settled. Aaron will meet me every day after breakfast to study. Do you agree, boy?" Aaron surprised himself by nodding. He could not take his eyes from the Great Rebbe's lumbering figure as he headed out into the late-day sun.

When Aaron had learned the whole Hebrew alphabet, his mother celebrated by baking sugar cookies in the shapes of the letters. When Aaron began to study Torah, the Great Rebbe rewarded him with a drop of honey to lick off the bottom of each page. And when Aaron himself became a rabbi, he spent a few minutes every morning picking wildflowers to decorate his classroom. He, too, wanted to make his students' learning as sweet as it could be.

⁂ 5 ⁑

Young Abraham

N o, no, no, *no, no, NO, NO!* I refuse to believe this!" Nimrod, the king of Ur, did not like what he was hearing. And when he did not like what he was hearing, he screamed and stomped his feet. This time, he stomped his feet so hard that the little statues around his throne wobbled and almost fell over. "Call in the next one!" he thundered.

"Sire, this is the sixth one you've thrown in jail today," the chief adviser murmured into the king's ear. "We're running out of wizards, and besides, they have all said the same thing, so it must be the truth: The dream you had of a star rising in the east and swallowing up all the other stars is a warning to you. The idol-maker named Terach will have a son who thinks for himself and worships his own God. He will destroy all our gods and be mightier than you, so mighty that an entire nation will descend from him." Then he lowered his voice even more. "You must find this Terach and stop the prophecy from coming true."

Nimrod ordered his soldiers to search everywhere, but it was too late. In the land of Ur, that rising star had just been born, and his name was Abraham.

Years passed, the soldiers never did find this special child, and Nimrod forgot all about his dream. And that would have been the end of the story, if it had not been for some of Nimrod's servants.

One day Nimrod found his servants whispering and laughing so hard that they were practically in tears. "It's not nice to whisper, you know!" Nimrod called. "Tell me what you're laughing about, please."

"Oh, no, Sire, we couldn't. It's just a story we heard in the marketplace today. It's nothing really. . . ." said one of the servants, wiping her eyes. "It's just that

some foolish boy went and destroyed half of his father's idol shop today."

Nimrod shrugged. "And what's so funny about that?" he asked.

"Nothing, Sire. Unless you hear the cockamamie story he made up to get himself out of trouble." Nimrod nodded, and the woman went on: "Well, the boy's father saw that all his idols were destroyed, except for one, a big one with a stick in its hand. So, the father was furious at his son, but the boy told him that the big idol got angry and wrecked all the others!" The women once again broke down laughing, and even Nimrod started to smile.

"Idols fighting with each other! Who ever heard of such a thing?" the other servant giggled. "Obviously, the boy did it himself! Can't you just picture that boy smashing all those idols and then telling his poor father. . . ."

By now, Nimrod, too, was doubled over. "Smashing idols," he chuckled. "Smashing idols!" He slapped his knee. And then, in the middle of a roar of laughter, he stopped. All the color drained from his face.

"Smashing idols?" he whispered. "It was foretold many years ago that a child would someday destroy our gods and triumph over me. . . ." Nimrod stomped his foot and called for his soldiers. "Find that idol smasher, and bring him here! Either he proves his loyalty to me, or he goes to jail—forever!"

This time, Nimrod's soldiers had no trouble finding Abraham. Just a few hours later, they led a tall young man with shining eyes and a calm face before the king.

"So you like to smash idols, do you?" Nimrod greeted him, as the whole palace looked on. "Well, let's see how clever you are now, my boy. Here is a god you cannot smash. Bow down before this fire, which I worship, or I will throw you in jail!"

Abraham looked at the pile of wood that burned in front of him. "Yes, Sire, right away, Sire. I will bow down to your fire god." Nimrod sighed with relief.

Then Abraham paused. "But wait," he said slowly. "Shouldn't I bow down to water instead? Water must be a more powerful god, since it can put out a fire."

Nimrod was impatient to have Abraham bow to any idol at all, so he answered, "Fine, fine. Guards, bring the boy water, and let him bow down to it."

This time, Abraham hesitated in front of the bucket that was set before him. "But wait!" he said again. "Shouldn't I bow instead to the cloud god that drops the rain that gives us water?"

"Very well, boy," Nimrod barked. "Face the clouds and bow to them, but do it quickly!"

But Abraham was not through. "The wind!" he exclaimed. "Surely the god of the wind is stronger because it can scatter the rain clouds away!" And he made a whistling noise, as if a storm were approaching. The people in the crowd began to murmur in confusion. Was it possible that all of their gods could be beaten by other gods? Then, who was the God who was powerful enough to rule over everything?

"Enough! I have heard enough!" Nimrod shrieked. He jumped up from his throne. "Let it be known that Abraham was willing to bow down to my gods," he declared in a loud voice. But, as he walked away, he stomped his feet one last time, not in pride, but in defeat. He could never tell anyone else, of course, but Abraham was indeed the shining star of his dream. With only the power of his own mind and a belief in one God, he had already destroyed Nimrod's gods, not by smashing his idols, but simply by doubting them.

❧ 6 ❧

Mazal Tov!

G ood morning!" Joha called brightly.

"What do you want this time, Joha?" came the cold reply.

Joha looked surprised. "Is that any way to greet your neighbor?" He ducked under her arm and into her kitchen before she could close the door. "Mmmm, something smells good!"

Joha's neighbor, Yasmeen, did not follow him. "I'm making lamb stew," she said, adding hastily, "and no, you cannot stay for dinner. We already have guests."

"Do you think so badly of me?" asked Joha, his wide eyes blinking in astonishment. "Do you really think I would visit just to wrangle an invitation from you?"

Yasmeen crossed her arms tightly. "Well, usually," she said. "But sometimes you want money, too."

Joha was already at the stove. "Well, you're wrong, my friend," he said, lifting the lid from a pot and inhaling the aroma inside. "Very wrong." He replaced the lid, stood back, and surveyed it thoughtfully. Finally, he sniffed, "No, this pot wouldn't do, anyway."

"What did you say?" his neighbor asked.

Joha had started flinging open cabinets. "That pot, it's too small," he said over his shoulder. "You see, I simply came over to borrow a pot this morning. I, too, am planning to cook lamb stew today!"

"You, cook? I don't believe it for a second!" said Yasmeen, following close behind and closing all the cabinets Joha had left open.

"Well, it's true," Joha shrugged, now peering into the pantry. "And I also have guests. In fact, I'm having many guests, and that's why I need to borrow a very large pot." He came out of the pantry with a triumphant smile on his face. "Like this one!"

Yasmeen narrowed her eyes. "Well," she said slowly, "if that's all you really want. . . ." And so, Joha left with her biggest cooking pot.

Early the next morning, Joha knocked on his neighbor's door.

"I've come to return your pot!" he told her, placing it gently on the table. "What kind of neighbor would I be if I hadn't brought it back promptly?" he said, noticing her surprised expression. "And look how well I've washed it for you!"

Joha was halfway out the door when he snapped his fingers and spun around suddenly. "Oh, how foolish of me!" he said, reaching into his pocket. "I almost forgot. . . ."

"Aha! I knew it," Yasmeen cackled. "How much money do you need this time, Joha? Do you owe the butcher for that lamb you ate last night?"

"Neighbor, really! Now, you've hurt my feelings," Joha answered, one hand pressed to his chest. "That's not it at all. I simply forgot to tell you the wonderful news! Last night, your pot gave birth to a beautiful baby pot, which, of course, also belongs to you." He pulled a tiny pot from his pocket and handed it to her. "Take good care of the little darling."

Yasmeen stared at the perfect little pot cradled in her hands. Pots having babies? How could it be?

While she was marveling over the baby pot, Joha cleared his throat. "I was wondering," he said, very respectfully, "if it might not be too much trouble to borrow a wine goblet. Just one, for again I have guests, and I'm one glass short."

"Of course, Joha," said his neighbor, as if in a daze. "Go ahead and borrow one. Just be careful with it." And so, Joha left with one of her fancy wine goblets.

Early the next morning, Joha appeared on his neighbor's doorstep again, grinning widely and holding out a bundle.

"My friend, you are one lucky woman," he said, laying the bundle in her arms. Here is the wine goblet you loaned me. And—*surprise!* A healthy baby wine goblet, too. *Mazal tov!*"

"Another baby?" said Yasmeen in a hushed voice. She carefully moved aside the blanket to see a tiny glass nestled next to her own goblet. Then she looked up into her neighbor's open face. "Joha, maybe I judged you wrongly," she told him, nodding slowly. "Listen, don't hurry off. Please stay and have some tea with me."

"Why, thank you!" Joha said, looking pleased. "Don't mind if I do!"

As the two sat down to drink, Yasmeen noticed that Joha was turning his silver spoon this way and that to catch the light.

"Joha, my friend," she said, leaning toward him, "don't be shy. You're having more company today, aren't you? Do you need to borrow that spoon?"

"It's like you read my mind," Joha exclaimed. "But I don't want to take advantage of your generosity."

"Nonsense! What are neighbors for?" she said, as she hurriedly opened drawers. "Don't just take one spoon—here, take two."

Early the next morning, Yasmeen was already waiting by the door for Joha to return with her spoons. And—who knows?—perhaps they might have given birth to some little ones during the night! The morning passed. Lunch came and went, and still Yasmeen waited.

By afternoon, she could wait no longer. She knocked lightly on Joha's door. "Is everything all right, Joha?" she called. "I expected to see you this morning."

"Oh, thank goodness you are here," Joha said soberly, pulling her inside. "I don't know how to tell you the news. Your precious silver spoons"—here his voice caught in a small sob—"they fell ill during the night, and, well, I'm sorry to have to tell you, but, but—" Joha's voice trailed off to a whisper. "They died!" He fell into Yasmeen's arms and burst into tears.

Her eyes welled up with sympathetic tears before she shook her head abruptly and pushed Joha away with a frown. "What are you talking about? How can spoons die?"

"Why not?" he answered indignantly. "If pots and goblets can have babies, then spoons can die!" He ignored her protests, patted her arm, and—murmuring "There, there"—led her back to her own house.

Joha returned home and poured himself some nice new wine from the barrel he had bought, just last night, for the price of—what a coincidence!—two silver spoons.

Joha raised his cup and announced: "To the memory of the spoons." He drank deeply, thinking, "They will be missed, but life goes on!"

✦ 7 ✦

The Bag of Trouble

I n New York City, on the Lower East Side, in an old apartment building, on the fourth floor, lived a little girl named Reina with a lot of trouble.

Reina had heard about trouble. Her parents and grandparents talked about it all the time, but they called it *tsures*. Whenever they noticed "Little Reina with the Big Ears," as they called her, they would try to change the subject. Still, she knew trouble when she heard it. She knew worried looks, wringing hands, arms up in the air. And she knew *tsures* of her own.

Like what? Like ever since her baby brother had been born, no one ever picked her up, unless she was hurt. Like spelling. Like brussels sprouts.

But even though Reina was little—but with perfectly normal-size ears, mind you—she was smarter than the grown-ups. She didn't let *tsures* bother her. Whenever *tsures* popped up, she just popped them into a bag!

That's right. She didn't fret, or scream, or cry, or complain, the way grown-ups did. Reina just crammed her *tsures* into a patched-up pillowcase and tied it closed with a sash from an old dress. She had kept her troubles from bothering her for a long time that way. Until now.

Now it seemed to take forever to walk the three short blocks to school. Past the old bakery, the tailor's shop, and the fabric store—Reina was already exhausted from trudging, and the day had barely begun! It was only when she looked behind her that she realized why. Ever since yesterday—when Goldie, her best friend, had become Molly's best friend instead—that bag had become enormous.

Reina's teacher was waiting for her at the classroom door. "Reinele, dear," she said, tapping the watch that hung on a chain around her neck, "you are ten min-

utes late. Where have you been? And what is that thing dragging behind you?"

"Oh, teacher," said Reina, collapsing into her seat, "I'm sorry I'm late. It's nothing but trouble, I tell you." It was a phrase she had heard often at home.

"Trouble?" Her teacher's stern face looked surprised. "Are you telling me a child like you has troubles?"

"You don't know the half of it!" Reina answered. The whole class buzzed with agreement, pouring out tales of their own *tsures*.

Finally, the teacher clapped her hands for quiet. "So, you've all got a lot of troubles, have you?" she said. "Well, classwork can wait. This is more important. Tonight, I want you all to go home and put your troubles into a bag like Reina's. Don't be shy—don't leave anything out. Tomorrow, bring your bags to school."

Reina squirmed in her seat. She didn't want to share her problems with the whole class. Those brussels sprouts had been crammed in there for weeks!

So on the way home from school, Reina snuck behind the fish store when no one was looking and flung her bag into the trash. There! That would get rid of her problems once and for all.

That evening, though, there was a knock at the door of her apartment. The fish man stood there with her poor, threadbare pillowcase dangling from one hand. "Reina," he said, handing it to her, "I think you lost this today." When he saw her open mouth, he added, "I just knew it was yours! I'd recognize it anywhere."

So the bag of trouble was back, a little heavier—and smelling like fish, to boot. Reina put the bag out on the fire escape and lay awake for a long time, wishing she herself could escape.

By the time Reina dragged her bag to school the next day, her classmates' desks were piled with string bags, paper bags, cloth bags, and a few pillowcases like her own. Some children had two of them.

"Teacher," Molly was asking, "what're we going to do now? Get rid of 'em?"

"Oh, no, dear," the teacher answered. "You can't just get rid of troubles."

"You're telling me!" Reina shook her head sadly as she sat down. "I tried that. They just got bigger and stinkier."

"Exactly right," said the teacher. "Here's my idea: Let's all open our bags, and everyone can look around. Who knows? Maybe you'll find someone who wants to trade."

"I'd trade in a minute!" thought Reina. "No one's troubles can be as bad as mine!"

The children were already scurrying from desk to desk. Reina looked into all the bags eagerly. There were more kinds of problems than she had imagined. A failed test here, a stomachache there. Someone's goldfish had died. Another's father worked so much that he was hardly ever home. Someone else's sister was sick all the time. Reina wasn't about to trade *her* troubles for any of those!

There was one bag left to investigate. Reina sat down, pulled it onto her lap, and peered inside. First, there was a scolding about forgotten homework. That wasn't terrible, Reina said to herself as she looked further. Chicken pox was next, then a spelling test, then a few other little things. Her face brightened. Finally, she had found a bag that she wanted more than her own! The *tsures* inside it were not so bad, and the bag even smelled a bit familiar, like brussels sprouts and. . . .

Reina smoothed the front of the bag, and her breath got stuck in her throat. She had been looking into her own patched pillowcase!

A few minutes later, she was done airing out the troubles inside. Her bag was very, very small now—small enough to fold up and stuff into her pocket.

"So, children," the teacher said briskly. "How did you do? Did you find someone to trade troubles with?"

"Teacher, I don't mean to be disrespectful," Reina said, "but I don't think that was such a good idea. If it's all the same to you, I'd just as soon keep my own *tsures*. They're not nearly as bad as I thought."

Soon after, her family began to wonder why "Little Reina with the Big Ears" seemed happier than she had in a long time. When they asked, she answered with a dramatic sigh, "Oh, I still have plenty of *tsures*, let me tell you. But I know how to handle them. The secret is"—here she lowered her voice—"they need company, just like anybody else! Take your troubles out once in a while, and let them get to know someone else's troubles. That'll keep 'em out of your way. Try it, and you'll see what I mean."

❧ 8 ❧

One Day at a Time

Shah Abbas, the king of Afghanistan, took off his crown. Then, he set aside his rings and all his fine robes. For a moment, he enjoyed the silent coolness of the midnight air. Then he put on beggar's clothing and crept soundlessly out of the palace.

Shah Abbas had everything in the world he wanted, and much more than he needed. But, oh, how he longed for something—anything—interesting to happen! So, lately, he had begun to stray far into his kingdom. He wandered unrecognized among his people, disguised as a poor man, to see what life was like beyond the palace gates. And on one of those nights, Shah Abbas met Koby the Cobbler.

He had just knocked on the door of a small house. "Is anyone home?" he called. "Can you please help the needy?" Koby opened the door at once and invited him in. Before long, they were sitting together, eating and drinking and chatting.

As they talked, Shah Abbas couldn't help but notice how spare the cobbler's home was. The table at which they sat was the only piece of furniture. A straw sleeping mat lay in one corner. The only food in the house seemed to be the bread and cheese on the table. And yet, everything about this poor man showed him to be quite happy.

"Tell me, Koby," said Shah Abbas, "what do you do for a living?"

"I'm a cobbler," Koby answered with a shrug and a smile.

"And what if no one's shoes need mending one day?" Shah Abbas asked. "What would you do then?"

"Hmm, I don't know. It's never happened," said Koby. "But I don't worry. I'm sure I'd be fine."

Shah Abbas nodded. "You obviously have great confidence in your king, that he will take good care of you," he said, proud to have ruled his land so well that even the lowliest citizens had no worries.

"Yes, that's exactly right!" Koby exclaimed. "But not the king you are thinking of, I bet. No, that spoiled and pampered man up there in his lofty palace does nothing for me." Koby leaned back against the wall and chewed on his toothpick.

Shah Abbas tried to remember that Koby had no idea whom he was talking to, no idea that he was risking his life by insulting his king. "Is that so?" said Shah Abbas through clenched teeth. "Then to whom were you referring?"

"The only king I have faith in—the one God," Koby said. He leaned closer to his new friend and whispered, as if revealing a valuable secret: "I live by the words of the psalm, 'Blessed be God, day by day'—and it has never failed me yet!"

But Shah Abbas was no longer listening. "I am not important to this little man, is that right?" he thought. "So, he thinks his God will always be there to help him, does he? Why, with one word from me, he can lose what little he has and be sent to prison, too, for the way he just spoke!"

For the next few days, at least, Shah Abbas had found a way to amuse himself.

Early the next morning, a royal proclamation was announced. By law, no one could mend shoes in the kingdom of Shah Abbas.

Shah Abbas returned to Koby on Friday night, once again pretending to be a beggar. After more than a week without work, Shah Abbas thought, he was sure to find poor Koby in despair. He peeked in through his window, expecting to see a sad scene. But he was wrong.

"Candles? Wine? Fish? Bread?" Shah Abbas was amazed at the array on Koby's table. "Why, this man must have turned to stealing!" He rapped loudly on the door.

"Oh, my friend, it's you," Koby greeted him, looking pleased. "How wonderful to offer you hospitality again! Thank you for letting me do such a mitzvah!"

"Thank you for having me," Shah Abbas replied, trying to keep his voice steady. "So, the shoe business is good, is it?"

"Funny you should mention that!" Koby told him. "Can you believe that pompous old windbag of a king outlawed being a cobbler? I guess he wants his subjects to enjoy only brand-new shoes! What a kindly ruler, eh?" Koby laughed and gave his guest a wink. "Anyway, the very same day I found some buckets, and I've earned my living fetching water for people all week. Here, drink this," he added, handing the Shah a full cup. "I spent my last penny on this wine. Isn't it good?"

"Your last penny?" Shah Abbas cried, spilling the wine all over his beggar costume. "And what do you plan to do tomorrow if no one needs water? Don't you think you should have set a little something aside, just in case?" Shah Abbas could still hear the words "pompous" and "windbag" pounding in his ears as he tried to wipe himself off.

"God will help me find a way, every day," Koby said. " 'Blessed be God, day by day,' remember?"

The next morning, a new royal decree was announced: Water carrying was now against the law.

By the time Shah Abbas knocked on Koby's door the following Friday night, he was sure that the poor man would be miserable. But Koby didn't answer.

"So much for hospitality!" thought Shah Abbas to himself. "I guess he needs me, after all!" But it soon became clear why Koby hadn't answered. He was too busy singing at the top of his lungs.

Furiously, Shah Abbas pounded on the door. The singing stopped.

"Three weeks in a row, now that is good luck," Koby said, opening the door wide. "Come in, come in and join me. I was singing 'Shalom Aleichem,' and you're just in time for the last verse. Let's see if we can do it in harmony!"

While Koby finished the song, Shah Abbas stared at the table, openmouthed. A feast was laid out! What's more, Koby was dressed like a—well, like a king.

Finally, the two men sat down to eat. "So, water carrying is a profitable business, I see," Shah Abbas said, helping himself to an artichoke.

"Actually, not at all," Koby confessed. "But let's not talk about business—it's the Sabbath! Eat, drink, sing with me. Later, I'll tell you what that stuffed shirt of a king has done now!"

"No, please, I'm so curious," said Shah Abbas, his anger catching in his throat. "Tell me what I— I mean, what that stuffed shirt did?"

"Well, all right. The very next day after you visited, our dear king outlawed water carrying!" Koby said, shaking his head and rolling his eyes. "Now, what could be going on in that mind of his, I don't know. So I took a little walk over to the palace grounds, where I have some friends among the servants, just to see what I could find out. Maybe the king is finally getting senile!" Koby elbowed his friend in the ribs.

"Well, you'll never guess. It seems that the king likes to play dress-up! That's right! He thinks no one knows that he dresses like a beggar and goes wandering in the streets at night. He doesn't realize he can't sneeze without the entire palace knowing, poor fool. Well, apparently, the last time he went on one of his little outings, the king managed to spill wine all over himself. The servants were terrified. What would they do if the king wanted his beggar costume again before they could wash it?"

Shah Abbas stared at Koby. He opened his mouth to speak, but nothing came out.

"That's when I got my wonderful idea!" said Koby, tapping his friend's knee happily. "I gave the servants my own clothes to replace the king's ruined costume. In return, they gave me this new outfit," he said, standing up to show off layers of embroidery and silk. "The kitchen staff even threw in enough leftovers and goodies to last me the whole week! Now what do you say to *that*?" Koby slapped the king heartily on the back and sat down on the floor, triumphant.

"What do I say to that? What *can* I say to that?" said Shah Abbas finally. "Blessed be God, day by day!" And the king returned to his palace, took off his beggar costume, and hung it next to his throne, where it would be a constant reminder that some things—like whether it was his destiny to wear a king's robes or a beggar's rags—are in God's hands alone.

✣ 9 ✣

It's All for the Best

ahum was a simple man. He could not read or write, he didn't hold an important job, and he wasn't wealthy. But to the people of his town he was practically a celebrity.

Nahum was famous for two things. First, he had extraordinarily bad luck. If he decided to sell umbrellas, it wouldn't rain for weeks. If a potted plant fell off a windowsill, you could be sure it would happen just as Nahum was walking underneath.

But do you suppose he was bitter? Not at all! A sweet smile stayed on his face even while the birds overhead used him for target practice. Always, he would say, "It's all for the best!" Never angry, never upset, just: "All for the best, all for the best!" And so, people started calling him Nahum All-for-the-Best.

"Tell me," a friend once asked in amusement, "how is bird poop on your head for the best?"

Nahum wiped his bald spot thoughtfully. "Well, if I hadn't needed to borrow your handkerchief, I might not have stopped to talk to you," he finally said. "And I do love to talk to you!"

No matter what happened to him—no matter how awful or nasty or just plain yucky—Nahum All-for-the-Best could somehow spin it around. That was the second reason he was famous. He was always happy, and that made everyone around him feel that, somehow, their problems might be all for the best, too.

So when the Sages of Israel wanted to send a gift to Caesar, the ruler of the Roman Empire, whom did they decide to send?

"Nahum All-for-the-Best, of course," said one of the wise men.

"Are you out of your mind?" said another. "He has such bad luck, something is sure to go wrong."

"Aha!" said a third. "But if anything goes wrong, who better than Nahum All-for-the-Best to handle it?"

"Exactly," said a fourth. "Anyone can have things go wrong. But only Nahum can make it turn out right!" So it was Nahum who set out the next day, his horse's saddlebags bulging with a gift of jewels for Caesar.

As night fell, Nahum stopped at an inn. Now, as luck would have it—or as Nahum's luck would have it, anyway—the innkeeper was a thief. All the loot that he'd stolen from his very own guests was kept locked away in a huge iron-bound trunk.

That night, while everyone was asleep, the innkeeper crept into Nahum's room, wrenched open his saddlebags, and stuffed the jewels into his pockets. Then he crept down the stairs and into the garden, where he shoveled dirt into Nahum's saddlebags so that his poor guest wouldn't notice how light they were. Finally, the innkeeper untied Nahum's horse and led it to his own stable.

The next morning, the innkeeper appeared with Nahum's breakfast and downcast eyes. "Sorry, my friend," the innkeeper said, shaking his head sadly, "but it appears that your horse was stolen in the night. I don't know how you can carry those heavy saddlebags all the way to Caesar's palace by yourself."

"Well, isn't this working out perfectly!" Nahum answered, as he tore off a bit of bread. "I was just thinking that I could use more exercise. So you see, it's all for the best!" And later that morning, Nahum set out again, swinging the saddlebags over one shoulder and whistling a little tune. He whistled and hummed all the way to Rome, unaware that the gift he was carrying was now utterly worthless.

As luck would have it—or as Nahum's luck would have it, anyway—he realized he had a problem only after he had made a magnificent speech before Caesar himself. "This gift from the Jews of my town symbolizes our feelings for you, great king," announced Nahum, with a bow and a flourish of one hand. He opened the saddlebags and dumped their contents on the gleaming marble floor. But instead of a flood of sparkling gemstones, a puddle of dirt dribbled across the floor.

"*This* is the way the Jews show their feelings for me?" Caesar growled. "Why have your people sent me such a gift?"

Nahum stared at the dirt. "I really don't know, but I'm sure it's. . . ." He gulped, and it seemed that, for once, he might not be able to make something good out

of something bad. Then he stood up straight and said firmly, "I'm sure it's all for the best!"

Dozens of Caesar's advisers swarmed around in a fury. "These Jews are making fun of you, Caesar!" cried one. "How dare they send dirt as a gift!" raged another.

Just then, an old bearded man stepped out from the crowd of advisers and scooped up a handful of dirt. "Your Highness," said the man, watching Nahum all the time, "perhaps this dirt is not an insult at all. I have heard the story of how Abraham, the forefather of the Jews, could tear down the walls of his enemies' cities with miraculous earth. It is said to be mightier than any weapon." He tossed the dirt against the nearest wall with one wrinkled hand, and everywhere the dirt touched, a burst of cracks appeared in the stone.

Caesar got up and let a handful of dirt trickle through his fingers. "Is that the meaning of this gift?" he asked Nahum. "Are your people offering me the strength of your great ancestor?" Caesar's face broke into a smile. "Then, what a wonderful gift, indeed! You said it yourself: It is all for the best!"

Nahum felt dizzy. Where had his gift of jewels gone? What was all this about magic dirt? How on earth was it that the ruler of the Roman Empire was clapping him on the back and looking pleased? It *was* all for the best, of course, but how? Just then, to make things even more confusing, the old adviser caught Nahum's eye—and winked!

Nahum was still a little shaky as he was sent home in a royal carriage, his saddlebags filled to the brim with even more precious jewels. And, most wonderful of all, he carried a letter from Caesar promising protection for all the Jews of his empire.

As luck would have it—or as Nahum's luck would have it, anyway—night fell just as he reached the inn where his horse was stolen. When the scheming innkeeper saw the magnificent carriage and overflowing saddlebags, his eyes bulged and his mouth hung open. "How did this happen?" he blurted out as Nahum climbed down.

"You'll never believe this," Nahum told him eagerly. "My saddlebags were packed with fine jewels, but when I got to the palace, they were filled with dirt! Imagine!" The innkeeper nodded a little too quickly. "The strangest thing is, Caesar liked the dirt very much—so much that he gave me a treasure worth twice as much in return! You see, even that dirt was all for the best!" Smiling, Nahum told the innkeeper good-night and went off to bed.

"This makes no sense!" the innkeeper thought to himself, over and over. Finally, he approached another guest—who, it turns out, was none other than Caesar's old, bearded adviser—with the astonishing story of the Jew who had just been rewarded for bringing dirt to the king.

The old man tugged at his beard and stared off into space. "I don't know," he finally said, "but if he gave that poor Jew a reward for two bags of dirt, imagine what he'll do for you if you bring a whole wagonload!"

On hearing this brilliant idea, the greedy innkeeper grabbed a shovel and ran outside. But as luck would have it—or as the *innkeeper's* luck would have it, anyway—he didn't notice the old bearded man transforming himself back into Elijah the Prophet. If he had, he might have thought twice about bringing a wagonload of dirt as a gift to Caesar. But it's all for the best. For insulting Caesar, the innkeeper ended up in jail—and that's where he belonged, anyway.

❧ 10 ❧

The Found Jewel

Most of the townspeople could remember exactly where they were and what they were doing the night the alarms sounded in their peaceful little kingdom. Trumpets blared, torches were lit, and messengers raced through the streets. Was it an invading army? A flood? An earthquake?

No. As it turned out, it was merely the loss of the queen's favorite diamond. Everyone was relieved, of course—except for the queen. To her, losing an exquisite jewel was far worse than any natural disaster.

"Find that jewel, do you hear me?" she raged at her attendants. "Find that jewel and the criminal who dared to steal it from me, or—or—or you'll all find yourselves in the dungeon! Is that perfectly clear?" The queen had a terrible temper.

"B-but, Y-your Highness, your most g-gracious M-Majesty," said the royal chamberlain, bowing low, "it wasn't stolen, it was just . . . misplaced."

"*Misplaced?!*" she shrieked. "How does one misplace a twenty-carat diamond?"

The chamberlain kept his eyes on the floor. "Y-y-you see, your jewels were being brought from your country estate to the palace, and the carriage overturned and rolled down a hill. Don't worry, though. No one was hurt."

"Get to the part about my diamond!" the queen interrupted.

"W-w-well, the trunk broke open, and everything spilled out. We found the emeralds, the rubies, and the sapphires. They were easy to spot in the snow. But not the diamond," he finished miserably. "We couldn't find it anywhere. It's impossible."

"Impossible for you, perhaps," came the frosty reply. "But I am the queen, and if I wish something done, it will be done."

The very next day, posters appeared all over the kingdom. "I hereby offer one million gold coins for the return of my diamond, no questions asked," the posters announced, "to whomever finds my jewel and returns it in thirty days, exactly, and not a second later." It was signed, "The Queen."

Now, it just so happened that the jewel *was* found. Thirty days after the queen's posters went up, it was discovered by a little boy playing in the snow near the road that passed the Jewish Quarter of the city.

"How wonderful!" cried his mother when the boy showed it to her.

"The queen will be so pleased, she'll give us the reward!" said his little sister.

"Pleased, indeed," said the boy's father, shaking his head. "Our dear queen might decide we're thieves and blame all the Jews for *stealing* her diamond instead!"

Soon, a crowd of neighbors had gathered, each offering an opinion. "Don't be a fool, boy!" said one. "We should hide the diamond and pray that the queen never finds it."

"We can't do that! That's just as bad as stealing it!" said another.

After much arguing, the Jews of the town did what they always did when faced with an impossible problem. They hurried down the lane and crowded themselves into the tiny cottage of Gittel the Wise.

Old Gittel sat and nodded as she listened to their arguments. The townspeople might exclaim or plead or wring their hands, but Gittel merely nodded more, pressing one finger into her wrinkled cheek.

When she had heard everyone's ideas, she nodded firmly one last time. "Don't worry, my friends," she announced, patting the table beside her. "Just put the jewel here, and leave the rest to me."

"But what will you do?" asked the little boy who had found the diamond. "If we don't return the jewel by midnight tonight, we won't get the reward."

"I know, I know," Gittel answered as she motioned everyone out the door. "The stone must be returned at the right time. Now, go back home, all of you. I promise everything will turn out fine."

Of course, the townspeople did not go back home. As the sun set, they pretended to admire Gittel's garden or to mend her gate, but, really, they were waiting for her to decide what to do. The later it became, the greater their impatience grew, until they could bear it no longer.

"What could Gittel be thinking?" someone muttered. "It's awfully late."

"Why is she waiting until the last minute?"

"Let's just take a little peek in her window and see what she's up to."

"Perhaps she's ill and can't get out of bed. Maybe we should go in and help her!"

Finally, they worked up the courage to look in the window. They found, to their great surprise, that Gittel was not getting ready to leave for the palace at all. No, instead, there was Gittel, sitting in her rocking chair, *asleep with a book on her lap!*

The townspeople rushed inside and shook her awake.

"Gittel, Gittel, what are you doing to us?"

"Are you crazy? Taking a nap at a time like this!"

"Don't you know it's already nighttime?"

"I know, I know!" Gittel said, sounding annoyed. "That's exactly why I decided to take a nap. I'll need one if I'm going to be up late tonight, don't you think? Now, *please* go back home."

But of course, the townspeople did not go back home. They stayed right there, shuffling their feet impatiently as Gittel stirred some soup on the stove. They stared at the old clock ticking away loudly from one corner as she slowly ate her dinner. They sighed as she carefully took off her apron, put on her shoes, found a fresh shawl, and smoothed a few white hairs under her cap. They nervously bit their lips as she wrapped the diamond in a fresh handkerchief, put it in her pocket, and patted it a few times. And then, *finally*, she left the little house and began the long stroll toward the palace. Just outside the palace gates, she paused and looked up at the clock tower. She did not rush ahead, even when the bells began to toll—one, two, three, four, five, six, seven times.

Gongggg! That was eight. The townspeople stared after her with open mouths.

Gongggg! That was nine. "Gittel!" they yelled. "Run!"

Gongggg! That was ten. "She can't possibly make it in time!"

Gongggg! That was eleven. "It's too late!"

There was a silence that seemed to last forever. Then . . . *Gongggg!* That was midnight. And then, *finally*, Gittel entered the palace gates.

From inside the palace, the queen, too, had been listening to the bells. Their ringing filled her with despair, for surely no one would ever return her beloved gem now. The echo had just died away when there was a low murmuring at her door. The chamberlain stepped aside, and Gittel entered the queen's chamber, holding out the diamond.

What joy! What ecstasy! The queen rushed to Gittel, grabbed the jewel, and covered it with kisses. At last, she caught her breath and pointed at Gittel, who was still standing in the doorway. "You there, I'll bet you're expecting that reward, aren't you?" the queen asked with beady eyes. "Well, old woman, you were too late. You didn't return my gemstone by the thirtieth day." She stroked her diamond. "Rules are rules."

"You're quite right about that," Gittel answered mildly. "Rules *are* rules. In fact, that's why I returned your diamond. My people—the Jews—have an important rule: Do not steal. And it would have been stealing to keep your jewel, which one of us found."

"Indeed," said the queen, nodding curtly.

"But you're wrong about my expecting to get the reward," Gittel continued. "In fact, I waited until it was too late—on purpose. Why? Because we Jews have another rule: Do the right thing just because it is right."

"Well, of course," said the queen, but she sounded a bit uncertain.

"Of course *you* know *that*, Your Majesty!" Gittel echoed. "A great queen like you—so well-known for kindness and honor!—*always* does the right thing. That's why you would like nothing better than to reward my loyal people—I know, I know!" said Gittel, shaking her head sympathetically. "Such a pity that you cannot do so, but rules *are* rules, even for a queen." She curtsied and turned to leave.

"Little does she know!" thought the queen, with a proud toss of her head. "I can do whatever I wish! I'll reward my loyal subjects, rules or no rules! This old woman can't tell me what I can and can't do! The only problem is . . . how can I reward them without breaking my own rule?" The queen sat for a long time, caressing her beloved diamond, lost in thought.

The next day, the queen ordered her chamberlain to take the reward of a million coins and to . . . ah . . . *misplace* a hundred of them in front of each home in the Jewish Quarter. This was not breaking her rule, the queen reasoned, not at all. A great queen such as herself—so well-known for kindness and honor!—could only do what was right.

❖ 11 ❖

The Lost Bet

Hillel was already forty years old when he left his home in Babylonia and traveled to Jerusalem to study Torah with the great scholars. It was not an easy life; he earned so little money doing odd jobs that sometimes he could not even afford to eat. But he got through the hard times with a little imagination, a little humor, and a lot of patience. And when his learning surpassed that of his teachers, he himself became recognized as a great sage. Even children knew who he was.

"There goes the famous Hillel," Zev muttered, nudging his friend as they watched the great man hurry past, on his way home one Friday afternoon.

"Oh, I've heard of him!" Asher answered. "My mother always says she wishes she had a little of his patience every time I get in trouble at school."

"That's nothing!" said Zev. "My father actually threatened to send me to study with him!"

Asher laughed. "I'd feel sorry for poor Hillel, if he was your teacher! Still, he's probably the only one who could straighten you out."

"Oh, you think so?" Zev's face wore a look that Asher knew well, one that meant trouble. "I bet he wouldn't be able to put up with me for long."

"What? You would study with him just to prove me wrong?" Asher asked.

"No, no, of course not," Zev said quickly. "I'll just bet you that I can make Hillel lose his temper. If I manage to get him angry, you pay me—say, 400 coins. If I don't, I pay *you*. Interested?"

Asher nodded enthusiastically. "Oh, this will be good," he said, and the two boys headed for Hillel's house.

Asher watched from behind a tree as his friend rapped on the door. "Hello!"

Zev yelled. "Is anyone home? Is there a man named Hillel here?"

There was a sploshing sound from inside, then footsteps hurrying to open the door. The great man himself opened it.

"Hello, young man," Hillel said, smiling through the water dripping from his beard. "What can I do for you?"

"Oh, no!" Zev said, trying to look sorry. "You were taking a bath before Shabbat. Don't be annoyed with me. I'll ask my question some other time." And he backed away.

"I'm not annoyed at all," Hillel answered. "You are already here, so go ahead and ask. What did you want to know?"

"Oh, well, I was wondering," Zev said, "why is the sky blue?" A little smirk peeked from one corner of his mouth.

"Hmm," said Hillel, "that is some question!"

"Now I *have* annoyed you," Zev said quickly. "What a—"

"No, no, you didn't let me finish," Hillel said. "I was just going to say that the sky is blue . . . the sky is blue . . . to match the sea! Yes, that must be it." He nodded goodbye in a friendly way as he shut the door.

Zev looked back at Asher and shrugged. He was not ready to give up so easily.

"Hellooooooo!" Zev yelled, more loudly than before. "Hello, Hillel? Help, Hillel! It's important!"

This time, when Hillel opened the door, his whole head was wet, but he still didn't look angry. "What is it? Is something wrong?" he asked.

"Uh, not exactly," said Zev. "I just wanted to ask you something else. You're not . . . *mad*, are you?"

"Of course not!" Hillel answered. "Ask, young man, ask."

"I was just curious," Zev said, "about why the sea is blue."

"Another important question!" Hillel laughed. "The sea is blue . . . so that we can tell it apart from the green land! *Shabbat Shalom!*" And he smiled and shut the door again.

Asher held one hand over his mouth to keep from laughing. "Zev," he whispered loudly, "are you ready to give up yet? You better have those 400 coins ready, because I think I've won our bet."

But Zev didn't answer. His face was red with anger—or embarrassment. He raised one clenched fist and pounded on the door. "Hillel, Hillel, Hillel!" he screamed. "Open up!"

This time, the door opened immediately. "I didn't get back into the tub," Hillel explained with amusement, "because I *thought* you might be back!"

Zev ignored that. "I had a question, a really important one," he said, scowling. "But I forgot what it was. Aren't you angry *now*?"

But Hillel just sat down on his doorstep. "Well, then," he said, "if it was that important, I'll sit here and wait till you remember it."

If Hillel was going to get mad, he would have done it already. Zev sighed heavily. "All right, I just remembered," he said.

"Go ahead," said Hillel, "ask."

Zev glared at him. "Are you the great scholar Hillel?"

"Yes, I guess I am," Hillel answered.

"Well, I hope there aren't any more like you!" Zev practically spit out each word.

"Oh, child," said Hillel, "why do you say such a thing?"

"Because you just made me lose 400 coins!" Zev stamped his foot and gestured at Asher. "I bet my friend over there that I could make you lose your temper, but it's *impossible*!"

Asher crept out from his hiding place and stood nervously next to his friend. What punishment were they in for now? Neither one of them could look Hillel in the eye.

But when Hillel spoke, his voice was as warm as ever. "You are really a very good student," he told Zev, smoothing his hair. "You have discovered for yourself that it never pays to lose your temper!" Then, grinning at them both, Hillel returned to his bath.

❧ 12 ❧

It's Not Fair!

I t had been a really long day for Elijah the Prophet. Exactly 10,324 baby boys had been born eight days ago. That meant that Elijah had to go to every single *b'ris* today. At least this one was the 10,324th. He sank down into a plush armchair covered with purple velvet, closed his eyes, and began to breathe deeply.

"Excuse me." A voice spoke to him from one side of his chair. "I'm sorry, but you shouldn't be sitting here. This chair is for Elijah the Prophet. He's coming to my little brother's *b'ris*, and he'll be here any minute now. So you should probably sit somewhere else." Through one half-opened eye Elijah saw that the voice seemed to be coming from a pile of curly hair, but he did not answer it. He gently wound a golden curl around his finger and discovered that it was attached to the head of a little girl. He smiled as her hair bounced back like a spring.

A pair of wide eyes appeared. "It's you, isn't it?" the girl said in a hushed voice. "You *are* Eliyahu HaNavi, aren't you? Oh, I just knew you'd come. My sister said you wouldn't come. She said you're just a legend. But I knew you'd come."

"I always do," Elijah answered. She was stepping on his toes in order to climb into his lap. "I was at your—oww, careful there—naming ceremony, too, but you were too little to remember. And don't get too comfortable," he added, "because this is the last *b'ris* of the day, and I've got to go right after the ceremony."

"Oh, sit for a little longer. I decorated this chair for you all by myself," she told him, her round cheeks turning pink. "Can't you stay for the party afterward? Don't you want some cake and wine? You know, you didn't drink any wine at our seder last Passover."

"Slow down, slow down," Elijah said. It was difficult to keep track of how many conversations they were having. "I *was* at your house at Pesach. And I *did* take a sip of wine, but just a tiny one. Why? Well, what would happen if I drank every cup of wine left for me? I would probably fall asleep before the night was even over! By the way, you did a great job on the chair. And now, it's really time for me to help hold the baby—"

Elijah tried to get up, but the girl wouldn't budge. "You said this was the last *b'ris*. And it's not Passover," she said, poking through his wiry beard, "so where else do you have to go?"

"I do a lot more than just show up for *simchahs*, you know," he answered. "I travel all over the world, fixing what's wrong, and trying to make things the way they should be. Some are big, some are little, but they are always important. So that's why I absolutely must. . . ." He tried standing up suddenly, but the girl, clinging to his neck, rose with him.

"Let me come with you!" She took his face in both her hands and pushed her nose right up to his. "Please, please, pleeeeeeeeeeeeeeease?"

Elijah knew he should say no. "I usually work alone," he started feebly. "How old are you—three?"

"Four and three-quarters. And I promise to behave well." She plopped a kiss on one of Elijah's eyes. "Thanks a lot!"

"All right," Elijah heard himself say. "I can have you back before the cake's all gone. But you must promise to follow one rule: You may not ask me any questions about my work, no matter what you see. Do you understand?"

"I understand and I promise," the girl said, and she let go of his neck.

Elijah closed his eyes and snapped his fingers. When he opened his eyes, they were standing in front of a dilapidated little cottage. The mailman was just pushing open the rusty gate to deliver a handful of letters. Seeing him, Elijah began to hum an out-of-tune melody. At once, the sound of a dog's growling rumbled close by. The mailman stiffened as he saw the huge dog galloping straight toward him. He threw the mail on the sidewalk and ran off at top speed. Elijah turned to the little girl and said, "All done here. Let's hurry, because I'm behind schedule."

"But—" the girl blurted. Elijah could see her mouth pinched shut with the effort of trying to keep her questions to herself. "It's not fair! Now that poor family's mail is lying all over the sidewalk! Shouldn't you . . . ?"

"Oh dear," Elijah said, as he glanced down, "I do need to fix that." He pushed

the gate open with his foot and began humming that strange melody again. The dog responded by bounding out of the yard, slobbering over an official-looking letter as if it were a pot roast, chewing it to shreds, and spitting the remains back on the sidewalk.

"Lovely, lovely," said Elijah, applauding enthusiastically. "Now let's hurry. I have one last stop to make before I bring you back home," he called over his shoulder. He guessed that the girl was standing there, her eyebrows pushed together, looking from the ruined letter to the terrified mailman and back again. But Elijah knew that the girl would not break her promise to ask him why he was doing such awful things—and having a good time at it, too.

Elijah snapped his fingers again, and the two of them were in a huge and richly furnished house. A man was talking angrily into the phone. "I don't care how poor they are," he snarled. "They pay almost nothing in rent, and I could make much more money if I rented that old cottage to someone else. And that's that!"

Elijah grinned and once again hummed his odd song. The door suddenly jerked open. A workman poked his head in, took off his grimy cap, and shouted, "Sir, you'll never believe it! While we were digging the foundation for your new house, we unearthed the most amazing treasure! Come and see!"

This time, Elijah was determined not to laugh out loud. "Wonderful. We're all set," he said gently to his young companion. "I think I can get you back home in time for cake." Elijah held up one hand, ready to snap his fingers again, but the girl stepped away.

"I promised not to ask questions, so instead, I'll *tell* you what I think," she said, folding her arms across her chest. "Everything you did was not fair! First, you let a dog chase away that poor mailman. Then you made him chew up an important letter. And then you gave that mean landlord a fortune! You said you helped people. But what you're really doing is hurting the good and rewarding the bad!"

Elijah tried to look stern, but it was no use. "You *did* see all those things, that's true. But what do they mean?" He held up one finger. "It didn't seem nice to make that dog scare away the mailman, did it?" he said. "His boss has been annoyed at how slowly he's been delivering the mail. But today he's running so quickly that I think he'll be on time. Wasn't that fair?" Elijah chuckled at bit, waiting to see whether the little girl would show some sign of approval, but she merely shrugged.

He held up a second finger. "Then I made the dog chew that important-looking letter to shreds, didn't I?" said Elijah. "But who wrote it? I'll tell you: It was the family's landlord, telling them that they would have to leave their home, because they don't pay him enough money in rent. The dog destroyed the letter, so that poor family didn't have to read it and worry over bad news tonight. Wasn't that fair?" The girl shrugged again.

So Elijah held up one more finger. "And then I allowed that same rich landlord to find a treasure. That didn't seem fair either, did it?" Elijah leaned a little closer to the girl, watching her try to guess how this one would turn out. "Money doesn't really make people happier, you know; they just think it does," he said. "But money is the only thing that landlord cares about. So, now that I've given him all the money he could ever want, he's completely forgotten about throwing the poor family out of their home. They'll be able to stay as long as they like, from the looks of things!" He raised one eyebrow. "Fair?"

The little girl stared at him a moment longer. Her arms relaxed. Her pursed mouth dissolved into a smile as she found herself back in her living room. And Elijah knew she understood, even though—for once—she didn't have anything to say. Just in case, though, he quickly offered her a piece of cake.

❧ 13 ❧

The Empty Fork

It is said that every Friday, on the eve of the Sabbath, two angels visit all Jewish homes and peek through their kitchen windows. If they see Shabbat candles lit and a table set with good food and wine, then the first angel—the kind one—exclaims, "May it be God's will that next Shabbat is the same!" The second angel, a cranky sort and a bit of a troublemaker, is forced to say, "Amen!" If, on the other hand, they approach a Jewish home and find it dark, without food or wine or any kind of Sabbath delight, then the disagreeable angel gloats, "You see? They have forgotten. They have all forgotten the Sabbath!" Then he makes his blessing: "May it be God's will that next Shabbat is the same!" When he says those words, they sound more like a curse. Anyway, the kind angel is forced to respond, "Amen!"

On this particular Friday evening, the cranky angel was feeling very confident. "I believe that's thirty-four homes so far, and not a single candle lit. Am I right?"

"Now, now," the kind angel answered. "Don't be so quick to judge them. After all, the law here in Russia won't let them practice Judaism. The czar has forbidden it." Still, peering inside the next house, the kind angel hoped beyond hope that perhaps *this* house would prove him wrong. But the tiny room was indeed cold and dark. An old woman sat alone at a table that was completely bare except for an empty plate and a fork.

By now, the cranky angel was already saying his blessing, while the kind one just shook his head sadly and whispered, "Amen." But something kept him from leaving the window. Perhaps it was the peaceful look on the woman's face. Her skin was milky-white, and though it showed the proof of her years, it glowed somehow. There was a faint smile on her lips, and in her eyes was a reflection of candlelight, although there were no candles burning.

The cranky angel called impatiently, "Come on! There's nothing there. Let's finish our rounds." But the kind angel could not forget this old woman.

A few days later, he returned alone. Once again, all was quiet. The fire in the hearth had burned down, and only a crust of bread and a glass of tea sat on the table. Yet the woman looked completely content.

He knew he was breaking the rules, but the kind angel flew into the house and stood close by the old woman. In her left hand, she grasped a pen, but she was not writing. Instead, she rested it on her shoulder, and her fingers moved up and down in a quick rhythm. Her foot tapped the floor, and her head nodded along. Suddenly, the kind angel realized he was hearing a violin playing, although there was no instrument in sight.

The old woman nudged her chair toward the hearth. Although only glowing ashes remained, the angel was quite sure he felt the warmth of a roaring fire. Although neither of them spoke, he was surrounded by the noise and laughter of a house full of people. And, although they were quite alone, he heard someone calling her in a sweet voice: "Natasha, it's time to eat!"

She moved her chair back to the table, put down her pen, took the crust of bread in her hand, and said a blessing over it. The kind angel was no longer surprised when the room filled with the scent of roasted chicken and soup.

"I'm coming, I'm coming!" he heard her answer, although the old woman's lips did not move. "But first I must do one more thing." Then the angel heard the rattle of coins dropping into an unseen *tzedakah* box.

The next Friday was also the first night of Chanukah. The kind angel was even sadder than usual as he visited Jewish homes. For each house he blessed, his cranky friend got to bless a hundred. Then they arrived at the home of the old woman.

"Come inside with me," the kind angel said. "It's early. And, besides, what have you got to lose?"

"It's against the rules," the cranky angel answered. "And, besides, what have you got to gain?" He looked through the window and saw no Shabbat candles, no *chanukiyah*, and no latkes, just an old woman sitting by herself at a table. "It's the same as all the others. What are you hoping for—a miracle?"

"Maybe so," the kind angel said, pulling his partner along behind him. They entered the little house.

"So, what are we waiting for?" the cranky angel demanded. "It's *still* cold and dark in here. Let's go."

"Shh," the kind angel whispered back. "Just watch."

The old woman closed her eyes and raised her empty fork to her lips. Then, her voice shattering the quiet, the woman exclaimed, "Ahhh! *Ochen vkusno! Deeeeee-licious!*"

The kind angel's eyes closed. He felt the thump of feet dancing to Chanukah songs. He heard an old man's voice telling the story of the Maccabees. He saw lots and lots of candles and shiny coins and dreidels. He smelled fried onions and potatoes. And, when he opened his eyes, he could still taste latkes.

"You're right!" the kind angel said. "They *are* delicious!" But the old woman didn't hear him. She just rose from her seat and went to lie down on her little bed, wrapped up warmly in her memories.

As the two angels turned to leave, the cranky one looked back and shrugged. "That fork *was* empty, you know," he said.

"Maybe so," answered the kind angel, "but I could tell that you tasted those latkes, too—admit it. And, besides, is the mitzvah just to eat greasy food? No, the mitzvah is to remember the miracle of the holiday. And I say that she remembered. The czar's rule won't last forever, but her memories and good deeds will."

And so, the kind angel said his blessing, and the cranky angel reluctantly answered, "Amen."

❧ 14 ❧

The Priceless Stone

L ong ago, when the Temple still stood, there lived a man named Netinah. Netinah was one of the greatest craftsman of his time, a maker of fine jewelry. He had a grown son who still lived with him, and they worked side by side in the jewelry shop. Though old Netinah was the owner of the shop, more and more it was Dama who ran the shop and cared for his father when Netinah's health was poor.

One cold and dreary day, Netinah went to the back of the shop to rest. Dama brewed himself a cup of coffee, trying to stay warm and awake. There had been no customers in the shop for days, and Dama's eyes were growing tired of watching the handle of the door. Only a few people hurried past in the misty rain, carrying groceries or bundles of firewood. Nobody, it seemed, was thinking about jewelry. No marriages were being contemplated, no earrings had been lost, no bracelets had broken.

Then, all at once, the door was pushed open in a whirl of damp air. Two men wrapped in heavy cloaks entered the shop. One of them placed an oddly shaped package on the counter. "Young man," he said, "we are here on official business. Go and get the owner of the shop."

"The owner is my father, but he is resting in back," said Dama, suddenly wide awake. "Can I help you?"

"No, no, this is far too important a job," said the man. When Dama opened his mouth to disagree, the other man said simply, "Show him." The first man hesitated, then untangled the straps that held the package closed. Layers of burlap, felt, and finally silk fell away, revealing a sight so gorgeous that for a moment Dama stopped breathing.

It was the breastplate worn by the High Priest in the Temple in Jerusalem. In the middle of a thick golden chain hung a square of pure gold. On this heavy slab, filigreed with dazzling designs, were arranged twelve sparkling, precious jewels— one for each of the tribes of Israel. It was the most important and holy necklace in the world.

The two men seemed almost relieved to reveal the secret of their package. "Now you know, young man, why we need to speak to only the most experienced craftsman," said the first man. "See? Here a ruby has cracked, and we must have it replaced. But it must be done perfectly."

Dama's mind raced. A job like this could bring in enough money to support his father and himself for years. It could bring in enough money for Dama finally to get married and buy a house. Enough even to raise a family of his own!

Dama tried not to show his excitement as he held the precious breastplate up to the weak winter light to examine it closely. "This is an exceptional piece of work," he told the men as he handled the breastplate delicately. "You've come to the right place. We have the kind of ruby you are looking for, and my father and I can make the repair right away."

Dama walked into the back room. His father was in a deep sleep in a chair next to a worktable. Dama put out his hand to shake his father's shoulder and wake him, but he hesitated. Lately, Netinah was waking several times a night, coughing, unable to breath. He would get out of bed and spend the rest of the night dozing in his chair. Dama watched his father's peaceful sleep for a minute more before returning to the men in the other room.

"I'm sorry, gentlemen," he said, "but you'll have to come back later today. My father is resting, and I don't wish to disturb him."

For a long moment, the men simply stared at Dama. "Don't wish to disturb him?" one of them finally burst out. "Think what you're saying! This is the breastplate of the High Priest of Israel!"

The other man said in a low voice, "Young man, we are prepared to pay you one thousand gold pieces for your work. Do you really think your papa would be upset if you woke him? He would be more upset if you let us walk out that door."

"A thousand gold pieces is a fair price," said Dama. "But you'll have to come back a little later." His mind was made up. Money comes and money goes. But Netinah hadn't rested in days, and Dama would not disturb his father, not for any sum of money.

The men stared at him, then turned away to whisper together.

"All right," said the quieter man, facing Dama again. "You drive a hard bargain. You know there is no other jeweler of your skill for us to turn to. *Ten* thousand gold pieces."

"Ten thousand gold pieces," shouted the other man angrily, "and not one more!"

His raised voice did exactly what Dama had not been willing to do. Netinah, awakened, stumbled from the back room, smoothing his hair and squinting.

"What's going on here, son?" he asked. His eyes fell on the breastplate that had been lying on the counter. "Who are these men, and what do they want?" he gasped, looking from one face to another.

"We simply want your help, and we offered to pay one thousand gold pieces," began the first man.

"Yes," growled his companion. "You should ask your son what *he* wants. He said our offer was fair, but then he tried to drive up the price!"

"That doesn't sound like my son," Netinah answered, his eyebrows furrowing.

"It's *not*, Papa," said Dama, exasperated. "I asked them to come back later, and they thought I was bargaining with them. But, really, I just didn't want to wake you."

"Ah, now *that* sounds more like the Dama I know!" laughed Netinah. "Well, gentlemen, I'm awake now, and my son and I will be pleased to do whatever work you require." And as he led the way to the workroom, he nodded proudly at Dama and gave his broad shoulder a little squeeze. "But we can accept only one thousand gold pieces if Dama already agreed to it," he added. "My son, as you can see, is a very honorable man."

Through the afternoon and into the evening, they sat close together, bent over the worktable. They spoke little as they handed tools back and forth, but their movements were as precise as the filigree on the breastplate, and their work together was as perfectly linked as the clasp that fastened it.

The next day, the breastplate was back at the Temple, around the neck of the High Priest. Dama and Netinah had worked so skillfully that the repair work was invisible. But whenever the High Priest called God *Av*—"Father"—in his prayers, the new ruby seemed to pulse and glow with a rosy light. It looked almost like a heart, filled with honor for a parent or with love for a child.

❧ 15 ❧

The Ladle

ne little, two little, three little fingers," the king sang happily to his grandson. "Four little, five little . . . uh, five. . . . Lord High Treasurer, what comes next?"

"*Six*, Your Most Excellent Highness, *six* little fingers!" called the treasurer through clenched teeth.

"Calm down, Lord Treasurer," the royal secretary advised as they returned to their work. "What does it matter if the king can't count past five?"

"Calm down?" came the furious, whispered reply. "How can *you* remain calm while his ignorance brings our country to ruin? The treasury is all but empty!"

"Ahh, but we can't blame him, can we? He *is* a fool, but that foolishness has helped us do quite well for ourselves," said the royal secretary. He fingered the diamonds on his ring and continued, "We'll just do what we always do. We'll sell off some of his jewels, or we'll impose a new tax. That usually buys us some time."

The lord high treasurer shrugged his shoulders in agreement. "Excuse me, Your Highness," he said as he approached the throne, "we hate to interrupt this delicious little game, but, if you will permit us to have a word with you, there is a matter of extreme urgency. . . ."

"Yes, yes, of course," said the king in a suddenly brisk manner, "if it is a matter of importance to the nation. Run along now, dear," he said, patting the little boy on the head. "Grandpa has to be a wise king now. My people need me!"

"It's about money again," said the lord treasurer, riffling through the pages of a ledger. "We need some. A lot, in fact. And we've just about run out of people to tax. If you'll notice here in the book—"

The king watched, bored, as pages of numbers and formulas sped past his poor brain. The more tabulations and columns he was shown, the louder he muttered to himself: "The book, the book. . . ." Suddenly, he jumped up and shouted, "Why that's it! I'm a genius! We shall tax the People of the Book!"

"What?" demanded the lord high treasurer, stopping short. "The People of the Book? Are you talking about the Jews? That will never work!"

The royal secretary poked the treasurer in the ribs. "Your Majesty, let me explain," he said smoothly. "These Jews—they aren't rich. They read and study all day. That's why they are called the People of the Book, you see. We will never get much money from them."

"Nonsense!" declared the king. "Haven't you heard talk of a man they call the Holy Lion in the city of Safed? He is just a scholar, but I hear he can perform wonders! Let *him* help pay the tax—or else!" The King's advisers opened their mouths to argue, but he waved them away. "I've made up my mind," he said airily. "As of today, these People of the Book are going to have a new nickname. How does 'People of the Tax' sound? Rather nice ring to it, wouldn't you agree?"

Word spread quickly of the king's new tax. The Jews would have to pay a thousand pounds of gold by the next day—or else! The People of the Book were taken by surprise. "Why us?" "What could the king want with us?" "We certainly can't come up with that money!" "What will become of us?" The anguished voices of the Jews rose into the night sky. They were carried by wind and sea thousands of miles away to the Land of Israel, where the man called the Holy Lion was listening.

There, in the desert to the south of the city of Safed, the Holy Lion began to dig. With furious speed, he dug and dug a hole in the sand with his bare hands. Then he lay down on the sand, reached inside, and began to pull something. He pulled with all of his might, his eyes squeezed shut. Finally, out of the sand he pulled a huge, gold-encrusted bed. And in the bed was the foolish king, fast asleep.

The man called the Holy Lion stared at him for a long moment. Finally, he tapped the king on the shoulder.

The king sat bolt upright, a sprinkling of sand pouring down his face. "Guards!" he cried hoarsely. Then, eyes as round as coins, he whimpered, "Where am I? Who are you? What am I doing here?" He clutched his teddy bear, pulled the covers over his head, and moaned, "Somebody pinch me, I'm having an awfully terrible nightmare!"

The Holy Lion gently sat on the edge of the bed. "Allow me to introduce myself," he said quietly. "My name is Rabbi Isaac Luria. I hear that you need a lot of money, and you want my people—the People of the Book—to give it to you. Is that right?" His calm tone reassured the king, who stopped trembling, peeked out of his blanket, and nodded.

"Of course, I'll help you," said the Holy Lion. "But you must do a little something for me in return. All right?" The king, beginning to feel a bit better, nodded more forcefully and even managed a smile.

"Good!" said the Holy Lion, grabbing the king's hand and forcing a ladle into it. "Now take this, scoop up all the desert sand, and dump it into the sea. By morning—or else!"

The king did not move or speak. He stared at the ladle, which was just the right size for spooning gravy onto a plate. Then he looked out at the endless sand. Finally, he looked into the face of Rabbi Isaac Luria and understood why he was called the Holy Lion, for his eyes held a ferocious pride.

"B-b-but, what you ask of me is impossible!" cried the King. "You know it can't be done. Please, I beg you, let me go! I'll do whatever you ask! Just don't hurt me!"

"I will not hurt you, but neither will I let you hurt my people," said the Holy Lion, turning away in disgust. "The tax you imposed on the Jews is just as impossible as the task I forced on you, is it not? Now, you will sign this document canceling your decree, or you will get to work with that ladle!" He held a piece of parchment to the king's face.

"B-b-but, I don't know how to write . . ." the king whined.

"Then use your signet ring," said the Holy Lion impatiently, dropping some wax onto the paper. "Just be quick and you may go." The king gratefully pushed the design of his ring into the warm wax and closed his eyes with relief.

When he opened them, it was morning, and he was back in his own bedroom. "What a nasty dream," he thought grumpily, shaking his head to clear it out.

He was in such a bad mood all day that he had no sympathy at all for the old man who appeared before him to represent the Jews. "I see you've come empty-handed," the king sneered. "That means you have failed to come up with the tax you owe me. Is that right?" he asked. He was proud of thinking so cleverly, all by himself.

"Yes, Your Majesty," said the old man, in a voice just above a whisper. "I have no gold. I bring only the prayers of the Jewish people that you will change your mind or that the Holy Lion will somehow save us from a cruel fate."

When the king heard Isaac Luria's name, his face went pale. Remembering how his nightmare had ended, he snatched up the document proclaiming the tax on the Jews. At the bottom was something that had not been there before: a smudge of bright-red wax embossed with the royal seal and the words: "I hereby cancel this document. It is null and void."

The King's heart raced at the thought that his visit with the Holy Lion had really happened. But he controlled his fear and said, "Relax, old man. I was just testing you. I know you are poor—Of course! Everyone does!—but you displayed bravery by coming before me anyway. And so, I wish to reward the trust of your people. Lord High Treasurer, give this man, four—no, five . . . uh, Lord High Treasurer?"

The treasurer looked uneasy. "Six, Your Majesty," he said.

"Six—thank you," said the king. "Please send him off with *six* trunks of gold."

❖ 16 ❖

The Wobbly Table

R abbi Chanina ben Dosa popped his head out the window and saw that it was raining. As always, the rain stopped as soon as he left the house, but Chanina didn't notice that. He also didn't notice that it started sprinkling again the moment he arrived back home. In fact, he didn't notice that he had not been rained on in years.

But there were many things Chanina didn't notice, like how a new coin always turned up in his pocket the minute he gave away his last coin to a beggar. Or how wilted flowers would perk up whenever he passed by. He wasn't thoughtless, exactly, he was just easily distracted. Chanina was such a holy man that he just spent all his time thinking about God and marveling at Creation. So he didn't notice the miracles that always happened to him, and he also didn't notice the regular things, like the fact that his children needed new shoes. No, for the details of daily life, Rabbi Chanina relied on his wife, Esther. So while the rest of the world was impressed with the great Chanina ben Dosa and all his miracles, Chanina ben Dosa was impressed with his wife.

Now Esther was a good person, too. But, unlike her husband, she had to *work* at it. When Chanina brought beggars home for lunch, it *bothered* her that there wasn't enough food for everyone. But she didn't complain. She just set out more plates and divided what little there was among them. When the children's clothes had holes in them, it *bothered* her that they couldn't afford anything nicer. But she didn't complain. She just smiled and mended them, again. Esther never admitted how it hurt her pride to be poor, pretending instead to be like her saintly husband.

But, the truth is, being poor hurt her deeply.

One Friday morning, she discovered she didn't even have enough flour to make challah. A few tears tugged at the corners of her eyes as she scraped the last bits of flour dust together. She couldn't make one loaf, not even a tiny one!

Well, maybe that wouldn't bother Chanina, but it bothered *her*. Maybe it didn't bother Chanina how the neighbors would talk if they were too poor even to afford flour, but it bothered *her*. Maybe Chanina would never think of putting some extra twigs into the oven so the neighbors would *think* she was baking. . . . Esther took a deep breath. And that is exactly what she did.

Soon, her oven was smoking very nicely. Maybe a bit too nicely, for before she knew it, her next-door neighbor burst inside. "Esther, come quick!" she cried. "I think your food is burning!"

"Oh, no, please don't open that d—," Esther answered, her voice wavering. But she knew it was too late. She hid her face in her hands.

"Don't cry, Esther," said her neighbor. "They're fine." Esther peeked through her fingers, and her mouth dropped open. Two beautifully braided loaves of challah sat proudly in the oven. "Perfect, in fact. Really, considering all that smoke, it's a miracle they're not burned to a crisp."

Just before sundown, Esther placed the two loaves on the table, moving as gently as a mother carrying sleeping babies. Rabbi Chanina did not seem to notice anything unusual about the challah, but Esther ate each mouthful carefully, trying to understand how this bread had miraculously appeared in her empty oven.

As the family went to bed for the night, Esther could hardly contain herself. The moment Chanina's head hit the pillow, she told him the whole story. "It's as if angels had done my baking for me!" she finished in a whisper.

"I'm not surprised, dear," said Rabbi Chanina, shrugging. "God just wanted to reward you. After all, you are the only reason I can live a life of good deeds."

"But just think," Esther said, her voice tiny with the hugeness of the idea, "if I'm being rewarded with such a favor, imagine how much bigger your reward would be! What if we asked God for some of *your* reward, Chanina? We'd never go hungry again!"

He rolled over. "That's not how it works, Esther. You can't just start asking God for things you want."

"Oh, I know you would never ask for yourself," she answered as if she hadn't heard him. "But wouldn't it be wonderful to be able to feed the children like this

every Shabbat?" She said no more, but she arranged the blanket carefully, as if the matter were decided.

There was a long pause. "Oh, all right," Chanina sighed, sitting up in bed. "Dear God," he began, "you know Esther and I always try to do what's right. And I'm sure that at the end of our lives, we'll be rewarded. But couldn't we have some of that reward now, so that we might be able to better care for our family?" They waited. Nothing happened. "You see, Esther, I told you that's not how it—."

Suddenly, with an enormous *whoosh* and *thump*, a huge thing crashed to the floor at the foot of their bed. They scrambled out from under the covers and peeked over the edge at it. It was a table leg, made entirely of gold and carved in a rich pattern of swirling leaves. But where had it come from? They looked up, almost afraid of what they might see, but there was no hole in the roof for the leg to have fallen through.

"Oh, Chanina, I told you!" Esther said, shaking with excitement. "Just because you asked, God sent us a table leg from heaven! Imagine what the rest of the table looks like!"

Rabbi Chanina and Esther talked through the night, planning how they could sell the table leg, and buy the children shoes, and give more to charity and. . . .

Well, they were so poor that it was a very long list. In fact, it was nearly morning when Esther finally fell asleep. But she could not stop thinking about the golden table leg. The moment her body relaxed, she began to dream about it. It was gorgeous, and the rest of the table—oh, it was huge, glittering, and carved all over with stars and planets, trees and flowers. In her dream, Esther noticed that there were in fact hundreds of golden tables, thousands, all gleaming with the reflected glow of a brilliant light. Angels went about their heavenly work, while others sat to rest. Esther watched them curiously, especially one angel who looked preoccupied. He was sitting at a golden table that wiggled slightly with his every movement. No matter how he tried to steady it, it still rocked annoyingly. The angel did not seem to notice that, while all the other tables had four legs, this one had only three. But Esther noticed. That magnificent table was wobbly, and she alone knew why it would stay wobbly forever.

Esther woke up gasping for breath. "Chanina," she whispered, "Chanina, we've got to give it back!"

"Give what back? What are you talking about?" he mumbled, rubbing the sleep from his eyes.

"The table leg from heaven. We can't keep it. If we do, an angel's table will be wobbly forever," she said. "And if he's distracted, think of all God's work that will go unfinished, all God's messages that will go undelivered . . . all God's miracles that will go undone." She sighed a long sigh. "If getting our reward means taking something away from an angel, it would be like stealing. And perhaps that is the same angel who did miracles for us in the past—and will do in the future, too! Then it would be like stealing from ourselves!" She nodded resolutely. "So you see, we have to give that table leg back. We can wait for our reward."

Rabbi Chanina looked at her with admiration and nodded back.

Esther concentrated hard. "Dear God," she said, "thank you very much for the golden table leg. But we can't enjoy our reward if someone else has to suffer because of it. So please take it back, and let the angels be comfortable and do your work."

They waited. Nothing happened. Chanina cleared his throat. "You see, Esther, I told you that's not how it—."

This time, there was an enormous *whoosh*, but no *thump*. When they opened their eyes, the table leg was gone.

While it's true that the family had to make do without the golden table leg, they didn't suffer. On the contrary. From that day on, the grateful angel rewarded Esther's kindness by making sure that her flour bag never again ran empty. Angels do deliver miracles for people all the time, but it takes a very holy sort of person to do a miracle for an angel.

❧ 17 ❧

My Friend, the Sea Monster

The ship's passengers had all but given up hope. They were stranded in a calm sea. They waited for the wind to pick up, but for the past two days, the ship had just rocked back and forth, going nowhere.

"So, Captain, a fine job you've done," a passenger grumbled under his breath.

"What's that?" the captain snapped. "If you have anything to say, stand up and say it out loud for everyone to hear!"

"All right, then," the man said, his voice rising. "I'll say it loud and clear: *This is all your fault!*"

A woman stood up and waggled her finger at both of them. "Now, just a minute," she said. "It's not his fault that we got stuck. At least *he's* given his share of food to others for the past two days—not like you, eating everything in sight!"

"Leave my boy alone!" an old man yelled. "He's still growing. And if he eats a lot, that's because he needs it!"

"And I suppose you need all that luggage, too," a voice from the crowd called out. "It's weighing us down. We should throw it overboard!"

The passengers were so busy arguing that they didn't notice that something much worse was still to come. Slithering toward the ship was the hugest, slimiest, ugliest sea creature in all the world. Oh, and she was hungry.

"Another bunch of stranded humans," thought the sea monster, as she swam right up to the side of the ship. "How lucky for me!" She licked her scaly lips and kept her eyes fixed on an apple barrel near the deck's railing. "When I help free them, they'll be so grateful that they'll give me lots of those delicious red things!"

Just then, a heavy wooden trunk came out of nowhere and struck the sea monster right between the eyes. "OWWW-OOOO!" she cried. The passengers, hearing that tremendous groan, rushed to find out whom—or what—they had hit. When they saw the sea monster rubbing her forehead with four of her tentacles, they panicked, screaming and running from one end of the ship to the other.

"What a way to treat me!" the sea monster sighed, shaking her head. "That's absolutely the last time I try to help humans." She lifted herself high up out of the water to get a good look at these unreasonable beings, and the people on board screamed even louder and ran to the other side of the deck.

"Now look what you've done!" one shrieked. "You made it angry by hitting it!"

"What *I've* done?" cried another. "*You're* the one who pushed me."

"You're both to blame!" yelled a third. "Oh, God, help us!"

"What a strange bunch these people are!" the sea monster muttered as she flopped back into the sea. "They treat each other as badly as they treat me. They ask God to save them, and when God sends help, they don't even recognize it!"

As the sea monster turned to swim away, she had the distinct feeling that she was still being watched. She looked over her shoulder and saw a girl hanging on to the deck's rail, a girl who was not yelling or screaming or throwing luggage. It was the captain's daughter, who had snuck away from the arguing to get a peek at the monster.

They eyed each other for a moment. Then, the girl blurted out, "You can talk!"

"Silly girl! Of *course* I can talk." The sea monster rolled her big black eyes. "And, as I *was* saying, I would be happy to get your ship moving again. But I just can't stand all that screaming and all those sharp words, so I'm leaving."

"Wait!" the girl said. "They're really not so bad. I'm sorry about that trunk hitting you." She reached up and grabbed an apple from the barrel next to her and offered it to the creature. "It's the least I can do," the girl said.

"Well, all right," the sea monster said slowly. "That's very sweet of you." She leaned forward and opened her mouth to take a bite, when suddenly:

"Look! The monster is going to eat the captain's daughter!" The screaming started all over again, and someone yanked the girl away from the railing.

"Stop, stop, stop!" the captain's daughter yelled, as loud as she could. "The sea monster isn't going to *eat* me, she's going to *help* me!"

There were a few chuckles from the passengers. "How do you know, little girl? Is that what the monster told you?"

"Yes," she answered, struggling to be released. When she looked out at the

water again, the sea monster was already slithering away. "Now look!" the girl cried. "You've all driven her away with your fighting." She looked at the apple still in her hand. "But maybe we can get her to come back." The girl threw the apple with all her might. It landed in the water in front of the sea monster, who suddenly stopped slithering. The girl hurled more and more apples, and finally the sea monster turned to face her. She hesitated. Then, cautiously, the creature began swimming back toward the ship, gobbling apples as she went.

"She could have eaten our whole ship if she wanted to, but she didn't," the captain's daughter called to the passengers behind her. "She just wanted apples. Quick, grab some more and help me!"

The crowd hesitated, until the captain stepped forward. He skipped an apple across the waves, like a pebble across a pond, and watched the creature nervously lick her lips. A passenger leaned toward the railing and sighed, "Poor thing, she's hungry, and now we frightened her."

The sea monster kept her eye on that tempting apple but stayed where she was. Someone called out, "Go on, it's all right. Go on and eat it."

Soon, passengers were tossing armloads of apples to the sea monster, and many more shouted out words of encouragement. Finally, the creature's face seemed to relax, and she began swimming toward the ship. "Maybe the girl is right," she thought. "Maybe they're not so bad after all."

When the creature had devoured every apple in the barrel, she dabbed at the corners of her mouth and smoothed her ruffled scales. "That was very tasty! Thank you all," she told the passengers, who were waiting silently to see what would happen next. She cleared her throat and bent down behind the ship. With the top of her head, the sea monster gently nudged the ship forward, and soon it was heading into a steady breeze.

"My daughter was right!" the captain cried. "The sea monster *is* helping us. Hoist the sails!" Without any hesitation, everyone got to work. The young men raised the sails. The old women made sure the children were safe. The passengers forgave each other for all the fighting.

The captain's daughter wanted to thank the sea monster, but the ship had already sailed far away, and the creature was out of sight. "I wonder what else sea monsters like to eat," the girl thought. "I'll just have to ask the next one I meet."

❧ 18 ❧

The Seeds of Honesty

L eah was bitterly cold as she trudged home one late afternoon. But instead of taking the shortest route, she climbed the road that passed by the Royal Gardens, just as she always did. Not so long ago, everyone in the kingdom had been able to walk freely through the gardens, enjoying the gracious lawns and marveling over the bushes clipped into animal shapes. But these days, the flowers and trees were guarded behind tall stone walls. Imposing iron gates offered only the tiniest view of the magnificent garden, which was now for the enjoyment of the king alone. Now, instead of walking through the garden every day, Leah could only peek through the cracks in the wall or boost herself up on top of it to see whatever she could. And what she saw today took her breath away.

In the middle of the garden, in a huge glass greenhouse, stood a tree of *gold!* Leah heaved herself higher over the top of the wall. The tree was tall but delicate. Wooden beams supported its branches, which hung heavily with shining fruit. She leaned farther and farther over the wall to get a better look, so far that she lost her balance and fell right onto a pile of wood chips on the other side.

Leah realized with horror that she had landed in the middle of the king's private garden. She knew she should climb back over the wall immediately, but that golden tree was just a few steps away. Whatever happens is worth it, she decided, if she could just see that tree. Before she could change her mind, she dashed to the greenhouse and eased the door open.

The air in the greenhouse was hot from the stone ovens that roared from every corner. Leah breathed in the intoxicating and unlikely scent of roses—roses, in the middle of winter! And there was much more. Crimson snapdragons and pink orchids, bleeding hearts and purple fuchsias exploded in color all around her.

But it was the tree in the middle that beckoned her with its sharp, citrusy aroma. As she got closer, she could see that it wasn't a tree of gold at all—but it was something no less amazing. It was an orange tree!

For a moment, Leah imagined that she was Eve in the Garden of Eden, her curiosity drawing her to one special tree. She checked to see whether anyone was approaching, and then she stretched up to touch an orange. It was covered with tiny lumps, and that smell. . . .

A hand fell on her shoulder. "Well, what have we here?" a guard growled. "A trespasser and a thief!" He grabbed her arm so roughly that the orange in her hand was yanked off the tree at the same time.

"Oh, I didn't mean to—, " she gasped. "I just wanted to—."

"Save your story for the king," said the guard, as he dragged her toward the palace. Once inside, he sat her down in a hallway. "Wait here," he said.

Leah turned the orange over in her hands. Well, she thought, whatever happens is worth it, if I can just taste this fruit. All her worries disappeared the moment she dug into the rind and a sweet burst of juice sprayed her face. By the time the guard returned to bring her to the king, Leah had eaten the whole orange. The seeds were hidden deep within her pocket, and an idea had begun to take root in her mind.

"Well," the king demanded, "how do you plead?"

"Guilty, Your Highness," Leah answered boldly. "One hundred percent guilty. I saw the orange, and I simply couldn't resist. That's the way thieves are."

The king looked surprised.

"So," Leah continued, "I accept whatever punishment you see fit. First, however, allow me to offer you a gift. It is my way of apologizing for having stolen one of your precious oranges."

The king found his voice. "Hah!" he said. "What can a girl with sticky fingers and fancy words possibly have to offer me?"

"A very precious gift, indeed, Your Highness!" she answered, stepping forward. "You see, I once saw an old man begging at the market. I did what any thief would do—I stole a loaf of bread and gave it to him. He was so grateful that he offered me a gift—these magic seeds." Leah held out the orange seeds from her pocket. "He told me that a tree of golden apples would grow if I planted them. But there

was a problem. The seeds could be planted only by a completely honest person—someone who had never stolen a thing. If a dishonest person tried to plant them, a tree of poisonous snakes would immediately sprout up." Everyone gasped. "So, it was a useless gift to a thief like me. But now, surely, I can offer it to someone here."

With that, Leah motioned to the guard who had arrested her. "Take them!" she said. "An honest man like you will be harvesting golden apples in no time!"

But the guard stepped backward and held his hands up, refusing to touch the seeds. "Oh, no, thank you all the same," he replied, tugging nervously at his cap, "but I don't think I should plant those seeds."

"I see," Leah said, nodding. She turned to the king's treasurer. "Well then, how about you, sir? I'm sure the treasury is full, but you can never have too much gold, can you?" she said, holding the seeds out to him. "*You* plant them."

But the treasurer also stepped backward. "Thank you, miss, for your confidence in me. But what if—by accident—I once made a mistake in the king's accounts? I couldn't be absolutely sure, you see. . . ." He kept his eyes on the floor as he said, "I don't think I should plant those seeds, either."

Finally, Leah approached the king. "Well, Sire, I'm sure you are guilty of nothing. You have treated your subjects fairly and kindly. I believe you must be the only honest person in the world!"

The king took the seeds, which still smelled a lot like oranges, and looked not a bit magical. To everyone's surprise, he smiled and leaned back in his throne. "Once, when I was a little boy," he said, "I was playing with my father's crown. A jewel fell out, and I kept it, without telling him. Silly, isn't it? When I could have had anything I wanted. . . ."

Leah just smiled back.

"And come to think of it, I may have taken something else that did not belong to me. I took something away from my own people, something they loved," the king said, adding, "Let it be known that the Royal Gardens will once again be open to everyone." He stood up and handed the orange seeds to Leah. "You won't need to climb walls anymore, young lady," he said. "And you are free to go. Just let me know when you find the person who is worthy of planting them."

❧ 19 ❧

The Bragging Contest

L ittle Caper Bush swayed in the cold night air. When the wind finally rested and the sun came up, she stretched her branches and stood up tall. Even through the chill, a warm feeling was beginning to stir inside her.

"Hah, hah! I'm first again!" she cried. "Oh, how I love spring. And how I love to be first!" Caper drew in a deep breath and burst open her first sprouts.

Proud Cedar Tree was waking up, too. "It's not a race, you insolent little bush," Cedar said loftily. "You may be first to sprout your cute little fruit, but I have *character*. Why, my wood was used to build Solomon's Temple!"

"Solomon's Temple, Solomon's Temple," Palm Tree mimicked. "That was *ages* ago! On the other hand, some of us are still useful." He loudly ticked off his qualities on each broad leaf. "My branches are waved during the *Hallel*. My fronds cover the sukkah. My leaves can be used for sweeping. And my fruit! Everyone knows that dates—"

"—have pits!" chuckled Etrog Tree. "Plus, you have no fragrance!"

Palm harrumphed. "You're just jealous because *your* fruit is remembered only once a year!"

"Fragrance?" Myrtle Tree called out. "Did someone mention fragrance? No one is more fragrant than I am!"

"Maybe so," Etrog Tree retorted. "Too bad you bear no fruit!"

"Well, at least I'm good for something!" Myrtle said with a toss of her branches. "Not like Willow over there. She has no fruit *or* fragrance. Maybe that's why she looks so weepy all the time!"

"Why do you always pick on me?" Willow sighed, as she stared at her own reflection in the water of a pond. "What good is fruit, anyway? Just look at

Grapevine. She can barely stand up straight under the weight of all that fruit. She needs to be supported, just like those who drink her wine."

"I wouldn't put it *that* way," Grapevine grumbled. "People say the wine made from my grapes makes them happy."

"True, but too much wine brings nothing but woe," said Olive Tree in his creaky old voice. "Now, the juice of *my* fruit is priceless! And long ago—you young folk don't even remember this—it was one of my branches that let Noah know the Flood was over!"

"Yes, olive oil is precious," said Pomegranate Tree. "Too bad they have to work so hard just to get a few drops! My seeds are delicious and juicy. And, did you know, I have 613 of them, the same as the number of mitzvot! Plus, everyone likes me, not like Carob, which only the poor bother to eat!"

"Oh, is that right?" Carob Tree said with a snort. "If I recall correctly, I was good enough to keep Shimon bar Yochai fed while he hid in a cave for twelve years! Besides, I don't recall that bragging is one of the 613 mitzvot!"

All the trees laughed at that remark, except for one. Little Caper Bush noticed Fig Tree's silence and asked her, "What do *you* have to say for yourself?"

Fig spoke dreamily, as if she had not heard any of the trees' arguments. "I was just thinking about how people love us. Have you noticed them during the fall harvest? They are so grateful for our last fruit before winter. Even when it's cold, they are still talking about us. 'Good people will flourish like the palm trees and grow like the cedars in Lebanon'—they sing that song all the time. In the spring and summer, people love us most of all. They see our buds blooming, or smell our fragrances, or taste our fruits, and they say, 'Blessed is God, whose world lacks nothing. Blessed is God, who created such beautiful things to make us happy.' " Fig paused and smiled. "That's all of us, my friends, *all* of us."

"You're right," said Caper. "You always are. Really, it's *you* who are the best."

"Me?" said Fig, laughing.

"Don't be modest!" Caper said. "All of you is edible, inside and outside. Why, even your seeds are good, even the smallest bit of you, just like the Torah. And just like Torah, you always teach us something new."

Fig looked pleased at this praise, and all the trees—the oaks in the hills, the palms in the valleys, the willows in the riverbeds, the sycamores in the lowlands, even the proud cedars and acacias, the oleasters and the cypresses—swayed together in agreement at last.

✢ 20 ✢

A Blessing Forever

Long ago, a man was traveling across a desert. He had made this journey many times before. Expecting the trip to last no longer than four days, he had packed enough food and water to last him that long. But on the third day, he realized he was lost.

On the fourth day, he ate less of his food and drank less of his water, wanting to make them last for an extra day or two. Of course, he would find his way soon. At night, he checked the positions of the stars carefully, trying to determine the direction he should take. On he walked.

On the fifth day, he slowly and reluctantly sipped the rest of his water and ate his last morsel of bread. When he searched the night sky, the stars no longer reassured him. In fact, he wondered if he was heading in the right direction at all.

By the end of the sixth day, the poor man had to search the bottom of his bag for the tiniest crumbs. His mouth was as dry as the sand under him, and his body shook with hunger and tiredness. He stopped walking. He stared at the horizon. There was only sand, sand, and sand. Now all the man could do was cry, but he was so parched that he could not even bring forth tears. In a hoarse whisper, he begged, "Dear God, give me the strength to go on. Show me the way home." Then he sank down on the sand. Evening came, and the stars began to poke through the purplish sky, as if urging him to continue. Gathering all the strength left in his body, he struggled, shaking, back to his feet and looked into the distance one last time. And he saw something his eye had missed before: a patch of green. Surely his weary mind was playing tricks on him in the darkness. But he stumbled toward the image. What else could he do? Before long, he could make out a big

and beautiful fig tree, with a flowing stream beneath it. He would not even let his eyes blink as he ran toward it, in case it should disappear from view forever. And then, there he was, beneath that tree with its heavy, luscious fruit. Standing in wonder on a little mound under the tree, he thought he could make out the lights of his town not far away. But he could not take another step. He fell at the edge of the stream and drank until his stomach ached. He ate figs until his belly bulged. Then he stretched himself out to rest for the first time in two days.

As the stars winked joyfully above the broad leaves, he was filled with wonder for the tree that saved his life. "How can I ever thank you? Shall I bless you with a clear, flowing stream to feed your roots? You have that already. Shall I bless you with abundant fruit? You have that already, too." The tree nodded in the night air, its leaves gently kissing the stars. Still thinking of how to give the tree a blessing, the man drifted off into a sweet sleep.

Those same stars visited him as he slept. In his dream, a strong gust of wind blew the stars from the sky. They swirled round and round, like sugar stirred in a glass of tea, until they came to rest in the sands of the desert. From each star sprang a tiny sprout, and each sprout grew until a family of trees stood proud and strong.

On the morning of the seventh day, the man awoke, completely refreshed and full of vigor. Right away, he remembered his dream and spoke tenderly to his friend. "Oh, tree, I know just how to bless you now! May you have as many children as the stars in the sky and the sands of the desert. And may each grow to be as beautiful and comforting as you are, to help all those who need you." Then he gathered as much fruit as he could hold, filled his water bag to the brim, and trekked on in the direction of the town ahead. He ate the figs as he walked, their seeds dropping from his fingers.

He was greeted with great happiness by the people of the town, who had feared that he would never return. He told the story of the miraculous oasis that saved him. Soon, other desert travelers, remembering his words, found their way there. And just like the traveler before them, they gratefully ate the tree's fruit, letting the seeds fall into the sand.

And so it was that the man made his blessing for the tree come true. In each place that a seed was dropped, a new tree grew, until the desert was green with a forest of life.

⚜ 21 ⚜

The Good-for-Nothing King

The king tilted his face up to the early-morning sun and inhaled the balmy air. He loved to go out in plain clothes and walk through the village streets, before anyone else was even awake, admiring the trees here, kicking aside some pebbles there.

"Ah, what a lovely peach tree," he said, reaching over a stone wall and helping himself to a juicy specimen. He gulped it down greedily and tossed the pit back over the wall.

And, then, suddenly, a tangled clump of weeds came sailing through the air and hit him square on the head. Before he could catch his breath, a clay flowerpot smashed at his feet.

"Who did that?" he cried, looking around. But he saw no one. Then a hand reached over the wall and tossed a bouquet of faded flowers, which hit him right on the nose.

"Aha! I've caught you!" he exclaimed, triumphantly grabbing the hand. It was tanned and callused, and the fingernails were caked with dirt. He yanked as hard as he could, only to find that the hand was attached to a beautiful young woman. A beautiful woman who was scowling at him.

"Let go of me!" she demanded, pulling her arm back over the wall with a jerk. "Who do you think you are?"

"The king, that's who!" he answered, before he remembered that he was in disguise.

But the woman just laughed. "Hah! The king, you say? Well, if you'll excuse me, *Your Highness*, I have to get back to my work. *Someone* had the nerve to steal one of my peaches and throw the pit back into my garden! Imagine that!" The king's face blushed the color of the peach he had stolen. "And you—you have to wipe some dirt off your *royal* shoes!" The mysterious gardener glared at him one last time and disappeared.

The king was left standing there alone, wondering who this woman was. With dirt still on his shoes and weeds still in his hair, he followed the garden wall until he reached the front door of a house.

He knocked on the door and called, "Hello? Could an injured traveler get some help here?"

An old woman hobbled to open the door. "Of course, young man, come in, come in," she said, motioning him inside. "Oh dear," she added, when she saw him more clearly. "Were you attacked? How did all this happen?"

"He was stealing—and littering in my garden, that's how!" called a voice from the next room. "And then, he claimed to be the king!"

"I see you've met my granddaughter, Manon," the old woman told him with a sigh.

The king nodded eagerly. "All right, so I *was* joking about being the king," he said. "But I wasn't stealing. I don't need to steal! I have plenty of money—all I need—right here." Out of one pocket, he pulled a money bag that clinked as he tossed it from one hand to the other.

"Really?" Manon said, poking her head into the room. "What a coincidence! I have everything I need in my pocket, too." She pulled out a packet of flower seeds that rustled as she fanned herself with it.

"Enough, you two," the old woman interrupted. "Let's sit down like civilized people and talk. Young man, tell us about yourself. What do you do for work?"

"Work?" the king answered. "My good lady, I don't need to work. As you can see, I am very wealthy."

Manon shot him a wide-eyed look. "You have no work?" she said. "Nothing? No profession? What do you do with your time?"

"I keep busy," the king said, nodding. "I take walks, and I enjoy the fruits—"

"—of other people's labor," Manon finished tartly. "And what would you do if your money ran out?"

"Oh, there's much more where this came from," he answered.

"How can you be so sure?" said Manon's grandmother gently. "You know what they say: 'Money comes and money goes, but a profession lasts forever.' "

"Nonsense," the king retorted. "Why should I learn to weave a carpet when I can buy any carpet I want? Why would I want to be a gardener and get dirt under my fingernails"—here, he picked up one of Manon's hands and examined it— "when I can hire someone else to do it?"

Manon stared at their clasped hands for a moment. "Why? Because I dare you to, that's why." She pulled away and pressed her packet of seeds into his hand instead. "I dare you to take these and make a living from them. I dare you to survive without relying on your sacks of gold. I bet you couldn't do it. I bet that, in one year's time, you would have nothing to show for yourself."

Manon's grandmother looked from Manon to the king and back again.

"You dare me, do you?" he said, quietly. Then he stood up and put the seeds firmly in his pocket. "Very well, then, I'll take your challenge. But, in one year's time, if you are wrong, then you must . . . *marry* me."

"Marry you? If you were clever enough to turn those seeds into a livelihood, I would be happy to be your wife," she said, shrugging. "But I don't think there's much chance of that."

A year later, the king had not only proved Manon wrong, he had proved her spectacularly wrong. He knew the names of every plant on earth. He could grow any flower, in any color or variation he wished. And he was an authority on raising fruits and vegetables.

On the morning he planned to ask Manon to be his wife, the king returned to her house, again in disguise. He wanted to see if she would accept him without knowing he was the king. But he was confident that she would, and he was filled with contentment as he paused at her garden wall. Now he had a profession, and soon he would have a wife. And just think, it had all started with a peach and a little packet of seeds—the same seeds that were still in his pocket, having long ago replaced the money he had once thought was so important.

But someone else was interested in the contents of his pocket—two robbers who were watching him from the side of the road. In an instant, they grabbed him and forced him into a waiting cart. "Give us all your money!" they demanded.

What use was it to tell them that he was the king? They would never believe him. What use was it to recall the purse full of gold he had left behind? It would do him no good now. He had nothing that could save him . . . or did he?

"I have no money," he told the robbers. "B-b-but I have a way of making money!" The king drew himself up proudly. "I am a master gardener. If you give

me time, I can grow the most rare and exquisite flowers. Then you can sell them for a fortune."

The robbers grudgingly agreed as the cart pulled up to a rundown house. "Here's your new job," they growled, pushing him into the garden and locking the high gate behind him. "Now, master gardener, get busy and grow us some flowers to sell!"

Not long after, Manon was taking her morning stroll through the market when she saw a new flower stall and vendors she didn't recognize. And, oh, what exquisite flowers they were selling! There were mimosas, lilies, and peonies of enormous proportions. She bought a whole basketful of vines and rushed home to plant them.

Later that night, as she sat in her garden listening to the crickets chirp, she noticed the blossoms on her new vines begin to unfurl. Slowly, three magnificent moon flowers opened. But what was more surprising was what she found inside: a little note that poked out of one flower as it unfolded. "Dear Manon," the note read, "I knew you'd like these. The night-blooming jasmine is nice, too, but these are my favorites. Well, you were right about having a profession, but you were wrong about me. I really am the king, and I do learn very quickly. And thanks to my new knowledge of flowers, I can tell you where I am. Now, you must quickly tell the police the flower vendors are my kidnappers so they can rescue me." The note was signed, "That good-for-nothing guy with no job, otherwise known as the king—and your future husband. P.S. I've grown a wonderful bouquet for you to hold at our wedding."

✤ 22 ✤

Joseph-the-Sabbath-Lover

*P*lop! That was the sound of one lonely potato dropping into Zohara's soup pot. And all it had for company was a turnip, a bone, and a sprig of celery. "Some dinner!" Zohara sighed. But she knew her husband wouldn't complain. He would come in as usual, gulp down his soup, kiss her on the cheek, and warmly thank her for another delicious meal.

"Joseph, dear," she began when he came home, "I'm sorry, but the soup is very thin tonight. It can't possibly satisfy your hunger anymore. Couldn't we buy a little meat today, instead of waiting?"

"Now, Zohara, you mustn't worry about me. Just hang on for one more day, and I promise we'll get wonderful treats for Shabbat." And he washed his bony hands and sat down to eat.

Zohara knew he was right. Tomorrow was shopping day, and together they would inspect all the stalls in the market. Everyone knew that Joseph saved every penny so that they could buy the best of everything for the Sabbath. And so the merchants would greet their old friend with anticipation. "Hey, here comes Joseph-the-Sabbath-Lover," they would say, as they presented their freshest and finest wares. "Look what I've been saving for you, Joseph!" So Zohara silently sat down next to him, and both were soon daydreaming about meat and pastries, wine and warm candlelight, all the while eating nothing more than watery soup.

Meanwhile, on the other side of town, someone else was dreaming, too. It was the rich landowner of the estate where Joseph worked. Now, this man should have been sleeping the sweet sleep of someone who knows no hunger or worry, but he was not. Instead, he was having a terrible nightmare: He dreamed that everything he had, everything he owned and loved, would be lost. And not just lost, but taken from him by a poor man with a ridiculously long name! He shook himself awake and laughed breathlessly, "Too much wine and spiced meat tonight, I guess! How could I possibly lose everything? And who in the world is 'Joseph-the-Sabbath-Lover,' anyway? Such nonsense." Then, promising to buy himself some stomach medicine at the market, he went back to his uneasy rest.

The next morning, the market was already bustling with its Friday excitement when Zohara arrived with Joseph. Her favorite part of the trip was watching the merchants treat her with great respect, as if she were the wife of a king, and not that of a lowly groundskeeper in patched clothing. "Those puny buds?" snorted one florist to another. "That won't do for Joseph-the-Sabbath-Lover!" And he presented Zohara with a few beautiful bouquets, awaiting her choice anxiously.

At the baker's stall, Joseph was eyeing some fruit tarts when the baker began teasing him, "You know, Joseph, you're not a rich man. Maybe you should buy something more . . . *economical*." And Joseph just laughed along with her and announced, as he always did, "Nothing but the best for Shabbat!" while he counted out his money. Soon, all the merchants and shoppers around him took up the chant: "Joseph says: Nothing but the best! Nothing but the best for his Sabbath rest!"

Now, the wealthy landowner was shopping for his stomach medicine nearby. "Are you all right, sir?" asked the herbalist when he saw how pale his customer had become. "Sit right down, and I'll make you a nice cup of nettle tea."

But the landowner stood where he was and asked, "Wh-who is that man?"

The herbalist followed his gaze. "Oh, that's Joseph. Everyone calls him Joseph-the-Sabbath-Lover," he said. "Every Friday, his shopping trip is the talk of the market."

"Yes," chimed in the butcher's assistant. "We save him the nicest things, and he never disappoints us."

"But how can he afford it?" asked the herbalist. "On the tiny salary you pay him?"

"I?" said the landowner with alarm. "What do I have to do with him? I don't even know this . . . this Joseph-the-Salad-Lover!" He was wiping away the sweat that had suddenly broken out on his forehead.

"But you must know him," said the herbalist, ignoring his mistake. "He has worked on your estate for years."

Well, that was all the rich landowner needed to hear. One of his very own workers, plotting to steal from him! Thank goodness he'd had that dream, he thought, clutching his stomach as it churned. Now he could outsmart that scheming Joseph-the-Salad-Scrubber. Or whatever his name was.

He went straight home and began selling his gold and silver ornaments, his animals, his house, and all his lands, everything—even his clothes. By the end of the week, he traded it all for a single precious pearl, a pearl so round and huge and perfect that he started to feel calm again. "Hah! Let's see that Joseph get his hands on what's mine now! I'm going to take my pearl and leave this place forever!" So he sewed the pearl into the lining of his one remaining hat and boarded a boat headed for a faraway land where he could never be found by Joseph-the-Cabbage-Scrubber. Or whatever his name was.

As the landowner's boat left port, a gust of wind suddenly came up and grabbed the hat off his head. As he watched, a gorgeous, shining-scaled fish leaped out of the water and swallowed that hat—the hat that held his perfect pearl—in one gulp of its lopsided mouth.

"Well," he thought, pounding his fists against his legs, "I've lost everything after all. But at least that Joseph-the-Cabbage-Grubber won't have it either."

Now, of course, Joseph knew nothing of the landowner's dream, or pearl, or hat. He was just minding his own business, working and living for Shabbat. At the market this week, however, he was getting disappointed. He and Zohara were looking for just one more dish that was special enough for their Sabbath table. It got later and later as Joseph wandered around and around the stalls, but still he didn't see anything he liked.

Just then, the most exquisite fish, with shining scales and a lopsided grin, was brought, fresh off the boat, to a fish seller in the market. "It's a perfect fish," he said to the fisherman, "but who will buy it at this late hour?" Just then, he noticed Joseph trudging one last time through the market stalls. "Nothing but the best," he thought to himself, and called out, "Joseph! Look what I have for you!" Joseph happily bought the fish at once, digging the last few coins out of the bottom of his pockets.

Joseph and Zohara went home to their tiny shack, cut open the fish to prepare it for cooking, and—what do you know?—found the most extraordinary pearl inside. They invited the entire neighborhood to celebrate their good fortune and had an even more joyful Shabbat than usual. The next week, they sold the pearl

for a lovely estate that had been put up for sale rather hastily, and they lived there in comfort and generously gave *tzedakah* for the rest of their lives.

And what about the landowner? It is truly a very sad case. You can still see him sometimes down by the waterfront, searching the waves for the grinning fish that swallowed his pearl. And every Friday afternoon, he gets a strange look in his eyes and starts muttering something about "that rabbit-scrubbing, cabbage-shoving, salad-grubbing sack of blubber!" Then he takes one last look at the water. "Or whatever his name is."

❧ 23 ❧

What Happened to My Chickens?

Esther punched the lump of dough in her bowl, angry just thinking about what an awful day she'd had. She plopped the dough on the table, recalling how the butcher had raised his price on chickens, which she now couldn't afford. She slapped the dough into a ball, recalling how some rude person at the market shoved her and made her drop the eggs she had just bought. She smashed the dough with the heel of her right hand, recalling the heel that had broken off her shoe as she slipped on a patch of ice.

One by one, she folded her troubles into the dough until they all disappeared. By the time a perfect braided challah lay before her, her shoulders had softened and her face relaxed. Now, all she had to do was cook the dinner and set the table and bathe the children, and *then* it would finally be Shabbat.

The moment she lit the candles, Esther closed her eyes, inhaled deeply, and let out a big long sigh. She was trying to hold on to that perfect, peaceful moment when she heard a most un-peaceful sound.

"Brrraaaak, buk, buk-buk, buk." Her eyes popped open. There it was again. *"Brrraaaak, buk, buk-buk, buk, brrraaaak!"*

Esther stared as two huge red chickens wandered in from the kitchen. They pecked at the rug. *Buk-buk, buk!* They jerked at the tablecloth until the *Kiddush* cup toppled over and wine rained down on them. *Buk-buk, buk!* The children chased the squawking birds around the table. *Brrraaaak! Brrraaaak! Brrraaaak!* In a moment, Esther's Sabbath peace had been shattered, by poultry.

When Chanina ben Dosa returned from the synagogue, he found a peaceful household, a hot supper, and a calm wife. "Esther, my love," he asked as he sat

down at the table, "did you notice what I left in the kitchen today?"

"Notice, dear?" his wife answered, pulling a few tiny feathers from her hair. "Was there something to notice?"

"Oh, Esther, you are wonderful," Chanina said, relieved. "Other women might be annoyed, but not you."

Esther smiled faintly and passed him the challah.

"Well," he began, "a farmer was driving some chickens to market, and he stopped to chat. He didn't notice that two of his birds had strayed into our yard. By the time I saw them, the farmer had long since left. But don't worry. I'm sure he'll be back tomorrow to claim them."

A week later, the farmer still had not returned for his chickens. Instead of pounding her challah dough to make herself feel better, Esther was pounding nails into a chicken coop they were building in the corner of the kitchen.

"Chanina," Esther asked as she hammered away, "do you suppose I might boil a few of those eggs for our dinner? We don't have much else to eat tonight."

"Eggs?" Chanina repeated. "Oh my, they have piled up, haven't they? But no, they're not ours to eat, Esther, you know that." He scratched at his beard thoughtfully. "On the other hand, we mustn't let them spoil. I'll bring the eggs to market and see what I can sell them for." He bent over the hens and patted them proudly.

A few hours later, Chanina returned, jubilant. "You'll never guess what I got at the market!" he called from the yard. Esther ran outside to find several huge sacks sagging against the house.

"Chicken feed!" he announced. "And that's not all. With the money I got from selling the eggs, I got two more hens besides!" Chanina hugged Esther around the waist and swung her through the air.

Esther was excited, too. "Oh, they couldn't have come at a better time! I can make chicken soup, or maybe . . ."

Chanina set his wife down gently. "We could never have afforded to buy the new chickens without selling the eggs of the old chickens, and the old chickens did not belong to us. They're not ours to eat, Esther, you know that. We'll just have to make do with what we have."

"Of course, dear," she said with a sigh. "I wasn't thinking."

Months passed, and the farmer still had not come back to reclaim his birds. After one sleepless night, Esther brushed some feathers off her husband's pillow and nudged him awake. "Chanina, what if the farmer doesn't ever come back to get the chickens? This can't go on forever, can it?"

"You're right, my dear," Chanina said, peering into one shoe before he put it on. "Look at the poor creatures, crowded together so," he added, as a yellow chick hopped out and scurried away. "I'll go to the market today and sell all of them."

Esther spent the morning sweeping feathers out the door once and for all. *Swak-swak-swak!* went her broom as she shooed every last bit of chicken-ness out of her home. She threw each window open with a victorious jerk to let in some cold, fresh air. Everything was returning to normal when she heard Chanina's voice outside. "You'll never guess what I got at the market!" he called. She looked up just in time to see him entering the yard with a rope in his hand.

Esther ran to the door, almost afraid to look outside. "You got rid of the chickens by buying—" her eyes followed the rope from Chanina's hand "—*goats?*"

The shaggy creatures stared back at her mournfully. "Husband, dear," she began in a low voice. "You don't *really*—." But the sound of footsteps crunching down the road stopped her from saying more.

"It's that farmer! I told you he would return!" said Chanina. "I knew you would come back for your animals, my friend," he told the man, holding out the rope for him to take. "And here you are!"

"No, Rabbi Chanina, I lost chickens, not goats," said the farmer, handing the rope back and looking hopefully past him into the yard. "What happened to my chickens?"

"Is that all you can say? 'What happened to my chickens?'" Esther asked in disbelief. She grabbed the rope and thrust it back into the farmer's hand. "We tended a whole farm inside our little house for months, and—well, of course, we didn't mind. . . . It was the right thing to do, but you might at least say thank you."

"Well, thank you, ma'am," the farmer spluttered, pushing the rope back into Chanina's hand, "but . . . what . . . happened to my chickens?"

"All right, I'll tell you," Esther answered. "We took them in and made them comfortable and fed them while we waited for you to return. And they laid eggs. But they were not ours to eat, and we would never take what wasn't ours." She took the goat's rope, put it back in the farmer's hand, and crossed her arms firmly.

The farmer looked at the goat. "So . . . what happened to my, uh, eggs?"

"You see," said Chanina, "under my wife's excellent care, your hens laid so many eggs that I had to sell them before they spoiled. And with the money the eggs fetched, I could buy more chickens and feed. And with all that chicken feed, the hens laid even more eggs. Then, I had to sell them all before they took over our house. And with the money we got. . . ."

The farmer's head swung back and forth, from Chanina to the goat, and from Esther to the little house, trying hard to understand what everyone was talking about.

Finally, Esther saw that they weren't getting anywhere. "Let me explain, young man," she said, gently pulling the farmer aside. "My husband is well-known as a very holy man. And he is such a holy man that he can make miracles. And for you, he has performed the miracle of turning your chickens into goats. Now, say thank you, take them—and have a safe journey home!"

Well, the farmer was so confused that he did just that. But to repay the couple for their honesty, he brought them gifts from time to time. No more chickens—thank goodness! Just little packages of fresh goat cheese, which went very nicely with Esther's freshly baked challah.

❧ 24 ❧

The Royal Test

The king of Morocco leaned closer to get a better look at the crystal ball. "Are you sure that's what it means?" he said doubtfully, squinting and pressing his nose against the glass. "*I don't see my prime minister leaving me. All I see is a little old beggar carrying a sack on his back.*"

"What?!" The fortune-teller grabbed her crystal ball and peered into it. "That was no little old beggar," she said as she wiped it with a corner of her veil. "That was just a smudge from your own nose."

The king shook his head as if he hadn't heard her. "Why would my trusted prime minister leave me for—for what? To join a circus?!"

"*Alakazaam, alakazoo,* that's what the crystal ball is telling you," the fortune-teller intoned mysteriously.

The king rubbed his eyes and stared into the crystal ball again. Finally, he gave up and sat back in his chair. "And I'm supposed to find a new prime minister by holding a contest? Isn't that what you said?"

"No, not I, Your Highness!" the fortune-teller cried. "*I am not telling you to do anything! The future—*" she paused dramatically "*—the fuuuuuture has spoken.*" She blew out her candles and whisked the crystal ball under her veil, making it seem as if it had disappeared. The king, who was always amazed at her special effects, dropped a purse bulging with gold into her outstretched hand.

The people of Morocco were used to hearing odd pronouncements from their ruler. So, the next day, when the king announced that he would choose a new prime minister by a contest of strength, no one was surprised.

No one, that is, except the old prime minister. "But, Your Highness, I am *not a* trapeze artist!" the poor man cried, stamping his foot. "I am *not* going to run away and join the circus!"

The king regarded him with pity. "You don't think so now, but you will soon. *The fuuuuuture* has spoken," he said, thinking of the crystal ball.

"Are you really going to replace me by holding a contest?" he whined.

"Now, now, don't worry about it, old man. Circus life is wonderful . . . the excitement, the travel. And just think: all the peanuts you can eat! Now, enough talk. Go and get representatives from every community, and bring them here so that I may choose the strongest!"

"What should the contestants bring with them, Your Highness?" the prime minister asked. "Weights? Dumbbells?"

"No," the king growled, "I already have one dumbbell, thank you very much! Just bring the people and a bowl of pepper. Obviously!"

"Obviously," the prime minister echoed in a flat voice.

The next morning, the town square was packed with contestants and spectators. Everyone wanted to see the magnificent displays of strength. But there was just one problem. There was still no representative from the Jewish community. The crowd grew restless until, finally, a slight man with a bald head elbowed his way across the square.

"I am here to compete," he announced in a timid voice when he finally stood before the king. "I, Joshua, will be the Jewish representative."

At first, the audience stared silently at this whisper of a man. Then someone began to giggle. Before long, laughter rippled across the square. "Why, this man can barely lift his own feet to walk!" voices from the crowd taunted. "This ought to be funny!"

But Joshua did not appear to notice the insults, and the king merely nodded. And so the royal test began.

The first contestant had flaming-red hair and stood nearly seven feet tall. "Your Highness, I am ready," she said proudly, rolling up her sleeves. "What would you like me to lift? Your throne, perhaps, with you still sitting in it?"

The audience roared with delight, but the king frowned. "How barbaric!" he said. "No, I don't want you to lift anything. Don't you understand? I need to find a new prime minister, not a furniture mover! I'm not talking about *that* kind of strength, muscle-brain! I'm talking about *character*!"

The tall woman looked confused.

"You *still* don't understand, do you?" said the king. "In order to find someone to help govern the kingdom, I need to find someone who can govern him- or herself—someone who won't have a temper tantrum at the drop of a hat, someone who won't burst into tears because of hurt feelings, someone who won't crack under pressure. Someone who can take a deep whiff of this bowl of pepper—and not sneeze. Think you can do it?"

The tall woman nodded uncertainly. She stepped forward, lowered her face to the bowl, and took a deep breath. Her face slowly turned as red as her hair as she wavered, and then . . . *HHHHHHHAAAAAAAAACH-OOOO!*

Her sneeze blasted the king right off his throne.

The next contestant was a man whose muscles bulged under his clothes. He put his face up to the bowl, but breathed in only the tiniest breath. After a long moment, he began to sway slightly. The king asked, "Are you all right?" but it was too late. The muscular man had barely nodded before he fainted gracefully into the king's lap.

And so it went all afternoon. As the sun began to set, the strongest men and women in Morocco had coughed, sneezed, wheezed, and gasped their way to defeat. Now, there was only one contestant left.

"Do you understand the rules?" the king asked in a tired voice.

"I think so," Joshua answered quickly. "Bowl, pepper, no sneeze."

"Very well, then, " the king said, waving a hand dismissively. "Get on with it."

Joshua put his face up to the bowl. He inhaled the pepper deeply and stood up straight again, facing the crowd. His eyes were watery, his bald head shone with sweat, and his nose twitched like a rabbit's. He opened his mouth, threw his head back, and . . . he . . . *sang.*

"Eliyahu HaNavi," he began softly. Then, stronger: "EliyaHOO HaTishbi, Eli-*YACHOO!* Eli-*YAA-ACHOO!* Eli-*YAA-AACHOOOOOO* HaGiladi!"

The king jumped to his feet and hugged Joshua. "Truly, here is a man who can control himself!" the king exclaimed. "Not only did he not sneeze, but he was able to sing through it all, too! This is the person I need by my side as prime minister!"

The crowd roared its approval, with the spectators from the Jewish community cheering the loudest. They had never heard "Eliyahu HaNavi" sung with quite so many AH-CHOOOOOs, but no one else needed to know that.

"So, tell me," the king asked Joshua as he led him back to the palace, "what song were you singing, anyway?"

"Oh, that," Joshua answered after he blew his nose loudly. "It's a famous song about the prophet Elijah—Eliyahu is his name in Hebrew. He lived a long time ago, but Jews believe that he still helps people when they need it, like me just now! He wanders around dressed like a little old beggar."

The king of Morocco stroked his chin. Little old beggar. . . . There was something familiar about that idea, but he couldn't for the life of him think what it was. Ah, no matter, he thought. He had finally found a prime minister who would serve him well. He didn't need a crystal ball to see that.

❧ 25 ❧

Purim in Chelm

J ews everywhere prepare for fun and games on Purim, but for the Jews of Chelm, it's different. For them, you see, joy is a *serious* matter.

It did not escape the people of Chelm that visitors always left their town laughing. They never really understood why, but it made them proud nonetheless. It must be a special gift from God—the ability to make others laugh—and they would not take this gift for granted. Oh no, they would cherish it and nurture it and *work* at it! So, while Jewish children all over the world were told, "No homework tonight—it's Purim!" the young scholars of Chelm hunkered down for the toughest, most rigorous part of the whole school year.

There were exams, late-night study sessions, and for older children, special projects. That's why Danny was awake at midnight, working alongside his brother.

"Oh, Danny, tell me again," said Little Max, chewing on his pencil. "Hamantaschen—who were they named after, again?"

"Ah, that was Queen Esther's pet dog," said Danny. "I know this stuff is hard, but keep trying. You'll get it. You're a Chelmite, after all." A few minutes later, he noticed Max furiously flipping through some pages. "What are you looking for now?"

"How many corners were there in Haman's three-cornered hat?" Max implored.

"Three—that's easy to remember because it's the same as the number of fingers on one hand," Danny explained patiently. "You think *you've* got it hard, but wait till you hear what *my* assignment is." He crumpled up yet another plan and tossed it into the overflowing trash can. "My class's Purim project is designing the world's loudest *gragger* to make the world's loudest sound! So when they read the *M'gillah*, you won't even be able to hear Haman's name."

Max looked at him in awe. "That's hard! What will you do?"

"Well, I won't give up, that's for sure." Danny stroked his chin thoughtfully. He was years away from having a beard, but he had already begun practicing. If he got good at it, maybe one day he would be one of the wise elders, just like his great-grandfather, who, it was said, had once captured the moon in a barrel. (Never mind that the moon had escaped when the water inside was poured out.)

Think, Danny, think, he told himself. What is the loudest noise you've ever heard? Was it the sound of Mom screaming when she found out you had used all her poppy seeds to lay a trail to school? That was loud. Was it Little Max crying when he realized he had sewn himself into his Purim costume and couldn't get out? That was pretty loud, too. But the world's loudest *gragger* would have to be even louder. Think, Danny, think!

Suddenly, he had an idea, the greatest idea ever. An idea so magnificent, it would assure him a place among the wise elders. He could hardly wait until the next morning, when he would announce it to his classmates.

The next day, Danny stood on a classroom chair and announced, "As you know, we have been challenged to make the world's loudest *gragger*!" The children groaned. "And I know just how to do it!" The children cheered. "But, I don't want all the glory for myself." The children *ooooh*-ed. "I can't do it alone, so I'll need all of you and all of your families to help." And then Danny told them his plan.

It was so simple, so logical. By the end of the day, everyone in Chelm agreed that this boy would surely grow up to be one of the great ones.

The plan was this: Everyone would collect as many stones and rocks as possible and put them in a big bass drum in the center of town. When Danny picked it up and shook it during the *M'gillah* reading, the noise would be earsplitting.

For three days, the people of Chelm collected stones and rocks. Even the littlest children collected pebbles. And so the drum filled quickly.

As the sun set just before the start of Purim, Danny and his friends from school met at the town square to carry the world's loudest *gragger* to *shul* for the *M'gillah* reading.

Danny walked around the drum a few times. It really was huge, and it looked even bigger now that it was stuffed full of rocks. After stroking his chin a few times, he rolled up his sleeves and grabbed the drum's rim. Struggling and strain-

ing, he tried to lift it. His face turned red with the effort. His friends circled the drum and tried to help. Even his brother, Max, grabbed the drum with his little fingers and heaved. But no matter how hard the children pushed and tugged, no matter how much they all stroked their chins, the drum wouldn't budge.

"Well, friends," Danny said, catching his breath, "I think the drum is too heavy."

"He's a genius!" Little Max crowed.

But Danny was not troubled by this setback. "Now, who remembers the riddle from math class last week?" he called out. " 'What weighs more: a pound of rocks or a pound of feathers?' Does anyone remember the answer?"

The children's blank faces stared back at him.

"The answer," Danny said very slowly, "is . . . *a pound of rocks and a pound of feathers both weigh a pound!* If they weigh the same, then it shouldn't matter what we fill the drum with! So let's fill it with feathers, and we'll be able to carry it to *shul* easily."

"Brilliant!" all the children shouted. "Let's do it!"

When they arrived at the synagogue, the adults of Chelm were already assembled, and the rabbi had begun to chant the *M'gillah*. Danny proudly rolled the drum up to the *bimah*. He could feel the eyes of the whole town watching him. When the rabbi neared the first mention of Haman's name, he nodded significantly toward the world's loudest *gragger*. Danny hoisted the drum into the air and shook it with all of his might. And. . . .

Nothing! Not a peep! Not a sound! Danny shook the drum harder and harder, but the feathers inside puffed and fluffed silently.

The gaze of the congregation now felt angry, not proud. Danny knew he had let them down, and on the most important day of their year, too!

The people of Chelm were speechless. The people of Chelm were furious. The people of Chelm screamed and stomped their feet so loudly that the ground shook. The earth trembled. In fact, Haman's name was entirely drowned out!

"Shuh! Shuh!" cried the rabbi. "You're so loud, I can't even hear myself think!"

This announcement stopped the crowd cold. When your brilliant rabbi can't even hear himself think. . . . The citizens of Chelm all realized what had just happened. "Danny did it! Danny did it!" they cheered, embracing him. "We made the loudest sound ever!"

And they swept their hero up onto their shoulders—Danny, future wise man of Chelm.

✢ 26 ✢

The Magic Donkey

Etty's black eyes darted back and forth across the edges of the market. What was she looking for? The usual—a dropped coin, a forgotten orange, an odd job to do. Once, when she'd found a lost child, she'd even been rewarded with a gold coin for returning him! If you knew how to use your wits, you could always make a little money. So Etty kept her eyes and ears alert for any little thing that would help feed her poor family.

What would she find today? Something, she hoped, that would make Purim a bit more fun. Everyone in the market was laden with hamantaschen and bottles of wine. Maybe, if she helped someone carry their packages, they'd give her a few of those lovely pastries. Wouldn't Mama be pleased to see treats like that!

Etty's visions of hamantaschen with gooey fillings were interrupted by the sounds of two men arguing. She crept around the corner to hear better. "What kind of servant are you?" a man with ruddy cheeks was yelling. "I send you to buy a donkey, and you come back empty-handed! Can't you do anything right?"

"How can I help it if there were no donkeys for sale at the market today?" a skinny servant answered angrily. "What do you need a donkey for, anyway? Isn't it enough to kick *me* around all the time?"

But his master was still shouting. "Now, go back to the market, and don't return until you've bought me a donkey!"

Etty hid herself again. In the few seconds it took for the poor servant to trudge past her, her brains were hard at work. She had come up with a brilliant idea, or at least half a brilliant idea. She ran straight to the rabbi's house and asked if she could borrow his donkey for the day.

"Certainly, Etty," the rabbi said, barely containing a smile. "What's the mysterious project this time?"

"I can't tell you now," she said, still a little out of breath, "but I promise we'll have a good laugh in the end." Then, leading the donkey by its rope, she hurried back to the market.

As soon as she spied the skinny servant walking through the crowd, she called out, "Donkey for sale! Donkey for sale!"

The servant spun around. "Well, I'm in luck. Just what I need!" he exclaimed. "How much for that donkey, miss?"

"How much have you got?" Etty asked, trying to keep her voice steady.

"The money's not mine," the young man said. "It's my master's."

"Well, then, give me half of what you've got," she answered, handing him the donkey's rope. "Maybe if you get a bargain, your master will stop being cruel to you."

The servant looked puzzled. "How did you know—?" But the moment he paid Etty, she smiled and ran off through the crowd without answering.

When she poured the coins into her mother's lap, Etty was so happy she almost forgot that she still owed the rabbi a donkey.

"And, Mama, we can buy wine and hamantaschen and still have lots left over to give to *tzedakah* and—" Etty stopped when she felt her mother's eyes studying her face.

"Come on, Etty," her mother said suspiciously. "Where did you get all this money? I'm no fool, I'm your mother, and you can't make a donkey of me. Out with it, girl."

"Make a donkey of you . . ." Etty repeated, almost dreamily. Slowly, the rest of her brilliant idea floated into her brain. "Oh, Mama, that's it!" And without explaining, she flew down the street, leaving her mother, bewildered, with a lap full of money.

Etty ran until she arrived at the master's yard. She silently opened the gate, tiptoed in, and removed the donkey's rope from around its neck. Speaking gently, she led it back to the rabbi's house, where she left it. Then, she returned to the master's yard.

She tied the donkey's rope around her own neck, took a deep breath, and—

"HEEEEEE-HAAAAAAAAAAAW!" She listened for a moment to see if any-

one noticed her braying. Then she let loose another "HEEEEEEE-HAAAAAAAAAW!"

Just as she'd hoped, the master and his skinny servant came running.

The master's mouth fell open when he saw her. "Who are you?" he blared, his eyes darting around the yard. "Who are you—and where is my donkey?"

"Oh, kind sir," Etty begged, clasping her hands and falling to her knees, "I am not really a donkey! HEEEEEEEE! I am a girl! HAAAAAAAAWWWW!" She pawed the ground, donkey-like, with one foot. "But I am under the spell—HEE-HAW—of an evil sorcerer! And I will remain like this—sometimes a girl, some- times a donkey—until my owner sets me free. It is the only way to break the spell!" Then she kicked up her legs behind her and brayed loudly again. "Please, sir—HEEEEEE—let me go!"

It was then that the servant recognized her from the market. "Aren't you the girl who—" he began slowly.

Fortunately for Etty, his master was even less interested in listening to his ser- vant than usual. "Go! Shoo! Quickly!" the master yelled, fumbling as he pulled the rope from Etty's neck. "Spells! Sorcerers!" he blubbered. "I want nothing to do with you! I'm setting you free! Just get out!"

Etty kissed the master on both his red cheeks, hugged the servant's skinny shoulders, and galloped off, braying and laughing at the same time.

"It figures you would bring home a magic donkey!" the master muttered, shak- ing his head and glowering at his servant. "That's the last time I give you an important errand. Tomorrow, I'll go to the market and buy a donkey myself!"

Well, as it happens, the next day, the rabbi went to the market to sell his don- key. The ruddy-faced master hurried over eagerly, but he stopped short the minute he recognized the donkey. He gathered his courage, marched up to the rabbi, and put his face close to his. "You there, you must be that evil sorcerer!" the master hissed. "Well, I know all about you—all about the donkey and the girl and the magic spell." When he saw the rabbi's confusion, the master leaned even clos- er and whispered, "You can't make a fool of me again! After all, fool me once, shame on you. Fool me twice, shame on me!" And the master stalked away, his cheeks glowing with ridiculous fury and wounded pride.

The rabbi felt laughter rising in his throat. Somehow—he couldn't imagine how, but somehow—he knew Etty was laughing right along with him.

❧ 27 ❧

The Other Me

Zelig decided it was time to leave Chelm on the day that his wife, Feigel, served him a bone for dinner. He opened his mouth to protest just as she realized her mistake. "Oops, sorry!" she said, flashing her most charming, gap-toothed grin. She bent down and wrestled the steak away from the dog, who had already taken a few excited bites. She brushed off the steak and placed it before Zelig, tossing the bone down to the disappointed dog.

"Sorry, sweetie," Feigel said lovingly.

"Who are you talking to—me or the dog?" Zelig grumbled.

"You, of course, my Zelig!" When Feigel saw him looking like that, her heart melted. In the dim lamplight, she could make out the single, thick eyebrow that stretched across his forehead. That eyebrow had made her fall in love with him so many years ago! It made him look so distinguished. Why, he looked like the wisest man in Chelm!

But Zelig was not in a loving mood. "I bet in Warsaw they don't serve a dog a man's dinner!" he muttered.

"Warsaw? What are you talking about?"

"I've been hearing a lot about Warsaw," Zelig said, nodding dreamily. "In Warsaw, the streets are paved with gold. In Warsaw, everyone is rich. Why, in Warsaw, they feed their dogs steak and, uh. . . ." He looked at his plate in confusion, but finished gamely, "They feed their husbands even nicer steak!" He paused dramatically. "And so, Feigel, I'm going to Warsaw. Tomorrow."

"And what about me?" Feigel cried. "Are you just going to leave me here in Chelm?"

"No, no," Zelig said, his face softening. "I'll be back before you know it. But, sometimes, a man's heart yearns for adventure."

Well, once a man from Chelm sets his mind to something, there is no way to change it. Feigel knew there was no dissuading him. But she also knew that he couldn't find his way out of a shoebox without her help. So, the next morning, when Zelig packed his bag, kissed her, and left the house, she followed him.

He walked through Chelm and into the forest. He walked and walked all morning, never realizing that he was going around in circles. Feigel, hiding herself a few paces behind him, knew better than to help; after all, a man's heart yearns for adventure! But, finally, all that adventure made Zelig hungry, so he sat down and had his lunch. And all that lunch made him sleepy, so he lay down to have a nap.

Now, Zelig was no fool. Before shutting his eyes, he looked down the road. "How will I remember which way I was going?" Fortunately for Feigel, Zelig always spoke to himself out loud. "If I fall asleep, I might wake up and head back home by accident," he reasoned.

Feigel whispered loudly, "Take off your shoes and point them in the direction of Warsaw. That way, when you wake up, you'll know just where to go."

Zelig snapped his fingers. "I know!" he said. "I'll take off my shoes and point them in the direction of Warsaw. That way, when I wake up, I'll know just where to go."

Feigel sighed. "Ahh, to be married to the wisest man in Chelm!" she thought to herself as she watched him arrange his shoes, lie down, and begin snoring.

There was nothing more for her to do but sneak over and turn his shoes around, so that they were pointing back toward Chelm. Then she hurried home, cooked a nice dinner, put on her best dress, and leaned out the window, watching for Zelig's return.

Sure enough, a few hours later, she saw her husband wander back into town, looking disappointed. "So this is Warsaw!" she overheard him grumbling right under the window. "Why, it looks just like home! The streets aren't paved with gold at all! I should have known better than to listen to such nonsense. How could any place be better than my own Chelm!"

He looked up and down the street. Berel the butcher was passing by and called, "Hello there, Zelig!"

Zelig stood stock-still, his mouth hanging open. "That man!" he murmured.

"He looks just like Berel from Chelm! And he called me Zelig! There must be another Zelig who lives here in Warsaw, and he must look just like me!"

"Zelig!" yelled the rabbi, who was passing from the other direction. "Zelig, what on earth are you talking about!"

Feigel heard Zelig draw in his breath sharply. "That rabbi!" he murmured. "Not only does he look exactly like the rabbi from Chelm, he also talks exactly the same way: 'Zelig, what are you talking about!' And he thinks I'm the other Zelig, too!"

Feigel realized her moment had come. She stuck her head out the window and called, "Zelig, dinner's ready!"

"Oh, no," Zelig moaned, bouncing up and down in a panic. "What am I going to do? She also thinks I'm the Warsaw Zelig, this other me! I'll have to pretend to be him!"

Feigel opened the door, and Zelig walked in and looked around nervously. Feigel followed his eyes: Here was a house that looked just like his own, a dog that looked just like his own, a dinner that looked just like his own, a wife who looked just like his own!

Well, once a man from Chelm sets his mind to something, there is no way to change it, so Feigel did not try. She motioned for him to sit at the table, which he did, awkwardly, watching her with curiosity. She smiled, kissed him, and gently put his dinner—a nice, juicy steak—on the table and tossed a bone to the dog. While he ate, she smoothed her pretty dress and gazed at her Zelig lovingly.

And so, Zelig decided he rather liked Warsaw after all. Which is not to say that he had forgotten about his life in Chelm. After dinner, Feigel heard him thinking—out loud, of course—"But if I am here in Warsaw, being the Warsaw Zelig, that means that back in Chelm the Warsaw Zelig is being the Chelm me. That's all very well, but what if the other me decides to come back?"

Feigel considered for a moment. Then, she whispered loudly, "What's the worst that could happen? If this other me returns, he will clear up the mystery of why you two are so alike. And," she added, grinning, "just think how he will thank you for taking such good care of the Warsaw Feigel!"

She watched Zelig's single eyebrow crease with concentration as he worked his way through her advice. Finally, his face brightened. "Good thinking!" he told himself and threw the bone on his plate to the familiar dog waiting patiently at his side.

✤ 28 ✤

Miriam Babysits

No one was surprised to see Miriam headed down to the river late one afternoon with a very big basket. She was probably on her way to wash clothes, or maybe collect eggs. That's the way it was with Miriam. She was always busy with some chore or other.

On this particular steamy afternoon, the other Israelite slaves were too tired to notice that her basket looked awfully heavy. The Egyptian slave masters were too bored to notice that she was singing a lullaby. Why should she, when the Israelite slaves had no more babies? After Pharaoh had decreed that all Hebrew baby boys were to be thrown into the Nile, the slaves themselves had decided that they would have no more children to suffer such a cruel fate.

Or had they?

The pile of blankets in her basket twitched. Miriam rearranged them, still singing. If the slave masters had been paying attention, they would have seen her stop at a well for a drink of cool water. They would have seen the basket twitch more, and they would have heard the unmistakable "wah-ha-ha" of a baby fretting. And they would have seen her smile at her pile of blankets, kiss them, and start singing again.

Miriam guessed the slave masters wouldn't ruin her plan, but the baby hidden in her basket just might. He was a pudgy, cheerful baby who never took his eyes from his sister's face. As long as Miriam kept walking and singing, walking and singing, he would coo happily, and she could continue. But if she stopped walking and singing—well, there would be terrible trouble if she were discovered trying to hide an Israelite baby. She needed to hide him—but where? If only she could find a kind Egyptian family who would be willing to take care of him.

At the river's edge she set the basket on top of the water. She watched it, until she was sure it was bobbing gently, then waded into the water behind it. When she was sure no one was watching, she started swimming, pushing the basket in front of her with one hand and then the other.

Miriam's sturdy legs chopped through the murky water with even strokes. After a few minutes, a little fisherman's shack on the near bank of the river came into view. Miriam hid her head behind the basket. Maybe this was the house of kind people who would take care of Moses. The baby himself seemed to read her mind, his quiet "wah-ha-ha" echoing off the water.

This caught the attention of the woman mending a net on the riverbank, for she looked up and squinted at the basket. "Husband!" she called back toward the shack, "someone has left a baby in a basket on the river. Should we rescue it?" A figure raised his head from the doorway. "Don't be foolish," he snapped, turning back to his work. "We don't need another mouth to feed!" As the baby began to cry in earnest now, Miriam pushed the basket hastily away from the shore and sang: "Baby, Baby, a fisherman you will not be! Don't cry, don't cry, we'll find someone to love you." And just as they always did, Moses' tears changed to gurgling.

At the next bend in the river, Miriam saw a much grander house surrounded by old trees. A woman in fine clothes was strolling by the river, a servant holding a parasol over her to keep away the late afternoon sun. Miriam's heart, already pounding, gave a leap. Could this be someone who would care for her brother? Again, Moses chimed in, "Wah-ha-ha."

"Ma'am," said the servant, shading his eyes, "I believe there's a baby in that basket. Should I go and rescue it?" The fine woman continued strolling. "Certainly," she called over her shoulder. "We could use another house servant." Miriam did not waste a moment, but roughly shoved the basket in front of her as she swam away as fast as she could. The sudden rocking must have surprised the baby, for he quieted at once, and Miriam sang, "Baby, Baby, a servant boy you will not be! Don't cry, don't cry, we'll find someone to love you."

Miriam's arms were beginning to ache, and her mind was whirling. What if she never found someone to take care of her brother? What then? The river widened, and the steps of a great stone palace loomed ahead. Enormous flowers floated on

the water, and servants in linen dresses hurried back and forth on the riverbank with bottles of oils and lotions.

One of them noticed her and shouted, "The princess of Egypt is coming to bathe, little slave! Take your laundry basket and go away!" Miriam kicked off again, so out of breath that she could sing no longer. Moses sent up a worried "wah-ha-ha." Now a different, softer voice called from the edge of the water, "What is in that basket?" The servant answered, "Nothing, Your Highness, nothing. Just a basket of laundry."

Something made Miriam stop swimming. She treaded water, holding the basket with one hand, so it would not drift away.

"Laundry?" said the soft voice, with a little laugh. "Laundry doesn't cry like a baby! Don't just stand there, go rescue the poor thing!"

But the baby, for once, was quiet. He seemed to be listening. The servant stopped wading and called back toward the bank, "Maybe it *is* just laundry, Your Highness. I don't hear a thing."

"Moses," Miriam thought, "for once, please cry! Let her know you're in there! This nice princess—I think she's the one!" But Moses had nothing to say.

After what seemed like a year had passed, Miriam bobbed her head under the surface and slurped a little water. She raised her head, carefully aimed at the basket, and spit out an arc of water that hit Moses right on the chin.

"Wah-ha-HA!"

"Finally!" thought Miriam. "For once, I'm happy to hear you cry!" She ducked back down in the water, hiding behind the basket.

The princess was wading out into the water herself. "Oh, little one," she murmured, gently raising Moses from the basket, "where is your mama?" The baby stuck his pudgy hand out of the damp blanket and grabbed one of the princess's long, thin braids.

With a sudden feeling of sadness, Miriam thought of where his mother was— she was sitting at home and crying, worrying that she might never see her baby again. This gave Miriam an idea.

She splashed up in the water as if she had been swimming past. "Oh, how cute!" she panted. "Do you need help with your baby, Princess?"

Moses was squirming now in the princess's unfamiliar arms. "I suppose I will need help, but you're too young," said the princess as she struggled to hold the baby, rearrange his blanket, and untangle her hair from his grip.

Miriam realized he was just about ready to burst into tears. Before she knew it, she was singing, "Baby, Baby, a prince of Egypt you will be! Don't cry, don't cry, you've found someone to love you." And, just as she had hoped, Moses was quiet again.

The princess was amazed. "Perhaps I was wrong, little girl. You certainly know more than I do about babies! How do I get him to stop crying like that?"

"Maybe my mother could help you," said Miriam eagerly. "She taught me everything I know about babies." She paused. "But, oh, she's so busy."

Moses decided that he really was hungry, after all. "WAH-HA-HA!" he burst out. "Go!" the princess shouted to be heard over the crying. "Go and get your mother, and I'll make it worth her time." Miriam swam off at once, her heart almost bursting with joy. Her plan, somehow, had worked. She was going to fetch her mother—Moses's mother—to take care of her own son!

The princess was pacing back and forth with the howling Moses over her shoulder when Miriam returned with her mother. The princess gave her the baby at once, and she sat down to feed him, her eyes brimming with happy tears.

Suddenly, everything was quiet again. The princess let out a deep breath. "I found this baby, the one thing I have always wanted but could never have. Feed him for me, and bring him here every day. He'll grow up to be a prince, so care for him as tenderly as if he were your own son."

Miriam's mother said nothing for a long moment. She stood looking at the princess as if she might hug her. Finally, Miriam nudged her, and bowing low, her mother put the baby on her shoulder and turned to go.

As they walked home along the river, Miriam found herself singing again. This time she didn't sing to keep Moses happy, for he had fallen asleep against his mother's shoulder, exhausted from his adventure. Now Miriam sang because she herself was happy. "Baby, Baby, an Israelite you'll always be. Don't cry, don't cry, we all will always love you."

❧ 29 ❧

Moses the Shepherd

Moses sat down to rest a bit while his sheep grazed. He could feel the scorching midday heat right through his clothes, and his eyelids squinted tight to shut out the sun's rays.

His thoughts wandered back to his old life in Egypt, just as they always did when he felt tired and his body ached. It was not so very long ago that doing a hard day's work had been a foreign idea to him, Pharaoh's favorite grandson. Had there really been a different life before this one—before he'd known he was a Hebrew, before he'd seen how the Hebrew slaves suffered, before he'd struck down that Egyptian slave master who was beating an old slave, before he'd run away and become a shepherd here, in the land of Midian?

Just then, a sheep bleated loudly, as if to remind Moses where he was. But through half-closed eyes, the flocks looked very much like the soft, woolly carpet that once lay in front of his palace bed, and before he knew it, he was drifting off to sleep.

"Baaah, BAAAH!" the sheep demanded. Moses jerked awake and looked around, but there was no cause for alarm. The baby sheep were finished eating. He always took care to lead them out first, so they could have the newest growth. Next, he let out the old sheep, so they could graze on soft grass with their weak teeth. And now, the young and strong sheep were making do with whatever the others had left behind.

One lamb bleated loudly at the edge of the pasture. I know, I know, Moses thought sleepily, you want to play. You are ready to move on, but we grown-ups

are not. Let them finish eating, and let me rest just one more minute. He closed his eyes again.

"*Baah, BAAH, BAAAAAH!*" This time, Moses was startled by the sound of little hoofbeats. He jumped to his feet and caught sight of a baby lamb just as it disappeared into some bushes. What was wrong? Had it been scared by a wild animal? He didn't see anything but the rest of the flock.

Moses ran as fast as he could. He scrambled after the lamb, down a long, dusty path. Finally, he skidded to a stop at the trickling brook where the lamb had stopped to drink.

"Hello there, little one," Moses panted, kneeling down beside the lamb. "I thought I'd never catch you!"

The lamb went right on drinking.

"So you were thirsty! But why didn't you just say so?"

The lamb looked up, blinking at him through its long eyelashes.

"Oh, you did try, didn't you?" Moses said, recalling the bleating that interrupted his daydream, "but I wasn't listening very well. I'm sorry. I was busy thinking of something else, when I really should have been thinking of you." He gathered the lamb into his arms, adding, "It's time to take you back to the others. You must be tired from all that chasing."

Now, God had been watching Moses, and noticed everything—how carefully he had let the sheep out to graze, how tenderly he carried the baby lamb back to the flock. God knew that only someone like this would be able to lead the Israelite slaves out of Egypt. And God thought, "Someone who hears the cries of the littlest lamb will understand the pain of the Israelite slaves; someone with a soft heart will understand Pharaoh's hard one; someone with no home of his own will be able to lead my children out of Egypt and back to their own land with patience and understanding."

At that moment, the sheep stopped bleating, the birds stopped twittering— even the breeze stopped blowing the grasses back and forth. God was getting ready to speak to Moses. And Moses, although he didn't know it yet, was ready to listen.

❧ 30 ❧

The Perfect Seder

hhh, what a night!" Rabbi Levi sighed happily as he settled down in bed. He felt warm, with his fluffy comforter, his huge pillow, and best of all, his perfectly clear conscience.

Rabbi Levi snuggled blissfully as he remembered his perfect Passover seder. In fact, this was his eighty-fifth Passover! He knew the entire Haggadah by heart. He knew every law about the holiday, every practice, and every custom. Rabbi Levi smiled as he closed his heavy eyelids and pictured Elijah's cup on the table. He chuckled to himself as he remembered his great-grandchildren opening the front door and refusing to close it until Elijah came in. And then Rabbi Levi fell asleep.

At least he thought he had, when suddenly a gruff voice called out, "*Gut yontif*, Rabbi Levi! Another fine seder, eh?"

Rabbi Levi was immediately as alert as if he had been splashed with a bucket of ice water. He couldn't be dreaming, he told himself, because he recognized the man sitting at the foot of the bed.

"*Gut yontif* to you, Elijah!" Rabbi Levi announced, beside himself with pride. Imagine! His seder must have been so good that the prophet Elijah himself had come to congratulate him. "And, as they say, 'Next year in Jerusalem!' "

"Yes, yes," Elijah answered, bending to adjust one of his sandals. "Next year in Jerusalem." His mouth crept into a sly grin. "Or at least at the home of Chayim the Water Carrier. I'm on my way to see him, actually. He's just about to begin his seder, and I don't want to miss a thing." In a flash, Elijah was gone.

The next morning, Rabbi Levi woke up feeling that he probably shouldn't have had that fourth cup of wine. His head ached, and he had slept hardly a wink.

"Chayim the Water Carrier? Chayim the Water Carrier?" he muttered all morning long. "What on earth did Elijah mean about Chayim the Water Carrier?"

Finally, Rabbi Levi could bear it no longer. He called together all his students and instructed them to search high and low for this mysterious man. "If this Chayim's seder was better than mine," he reasoned aloud, "he must be a very righteous *tzaddik*. Maybe he's even a *lamed-vavnik*, one of the thirty-six righteous souls the whole world depends on!" Rabbi Levi jumped out of his armchair and paced back and forth. "He must be one in a million!" He tried to calm himself and settled down for a long wait. This great man would be hard to find.

But only ten minutes later, the students returned with none other than Chayim the Water Carrier, a thin, stooped man with a few wispy hairs on the top of his head. It so happened that Chayim lived right next door to Rabbi Levi, although the rabbi had never noticed him.

"So, you are Chayim the Water Carrier! I've heard great things about you!" Rabbi Levi said, shaking his hand warmly. "Tell me, please, all about your seder last night. Don't leave out a single detail!"

"My seder?" Chayim repeated, his voice breathless. Suddenly, he fell to his knees, crying and kissing Rabbi Levi's hand. "Oh, Rabbi, please don't call the police. I swear I have no idea where that food came from! Or the silver wine goblet, or the silver candlesticks. I can return all of it, except for the food, of course, because I ate that up," Chayim blubbered. "Please, Rabbi Levi, I am no thief!"

"Relax, my friend," Rabbi Levi said, pulling the poor man off the floor and into a chair. "I'm not accusing you of anything. What food? What silver? Tell me what happened."

"Well," Chayim said, his voice still quavering, "this year, I intended to keep Passover faithfully, I really did! I knew whiskey is not kosher for Passover, so I began my holiday cleaning by drinking it all up. And then, I meant to have a seder, I really did, but the whiskey must have made me sleepy. Around midnight, my wife finally pokes me in the ribs and says, 'Chayim! Why don't you wake up and have a seder like every other Jew in the world!'

"So I say to her: 'Dear, I'm just a poor, ignorant man. All I know is that once we were slaves, and God freed us!' " Chayim paused, surveying the spellbound faces of the great rabbi and all his students. Then he added in a loud whisper, "That's when—that's when it happened."

"When what happened?" Rabbi Levi demanded.

Chayim closed his eyes as if remembering the scene and continued, "Suddenly, the table was filled with food and wine and silver—silver so shiny it made my eyes tear!" He looked at Rabbi Levi and confided, "Of course, I thought the whiskey was playing tricks on me. So I say to my wife, 'Where did this come from? Is it real?' She says, 'Real or not, let's eat!' So I listened to her, since she has always been smarter than me. But, I swear, I didn't steal those things! They just—appeared!"

Rabbi Levi ignored his protest. "But the seder—surely, you went on to follow every step of the seder? You read every word of the Haggadah?" he prompted.

"No, actually," answered Chayim, squirming with embarrassment. "I can't read."

Rabbi Levi's mouth fell open. Could he have found the wrong Chayim? "Are you *sure* you didn't do anything else?" he asked

Chayim thought for a moment. "Well, after we ate, I did say: 'God, thank You for this wonderful feast. But you know, in a way we are still slaves! There is poverty, injustice, and war all around us. You freed us then—may You show us the way to freedom again!' And that's when a little old man wearing sandals walked in and said, 'Amen!' " Chayim shook his head and said, "Sandals! Oh, it's so crazy, I'm sure you don't believe me."

Rabbi Levi nodded as he sat back in his chair, remembering how Elijah had been in a rush to get to Chayim's seder. And now he knew why. Of the fourteen steps of a regular seder, of the hundreds of rituals and the thousands of commentaries—of all these Passover details, Chayim knew only two things: that God freed the Israelites from slavery, and that the world still needs work. That was all, and that was enough.

"Anything else?" Rabbi Levi asked Chayim.

"Well, I think I fell asleep again until your students woke me up and brought me here," said Chayim, turning nervous again. "So, tell me, am I in some sort of trouble?"

"No, my friend, not at all," Rabbi Levi said. "After eighty-five years, I feel like I, too, have woken up. Next year in Jerusalem!" he added. "Or, at least, at your house."

⚘ 31 ⚘

Nachshon and the Sea

When the Israelites were slaves in Egypt, they were used to feeling tired, because they had to work day and night, building enormous pyramids for a cruel Pharaoh. They were used to feeling hungry, for Pharaoh made sure they never had enough to eat. And they were used to feeling sad, knowing that their children would grow up as slaves, just as their fathers and mothers before them had for four hundred years.

So when God heard their cries and freed them from slavery, the Children of Israel felt a new feeling: excitement. Slaves never feel excited. Every day is like every other day. Why bother to think or plan or hope? But now they were learning to do all these things—in a hurry.

True, when they left Egypt, they still *looked* like slaves, in ragged clothes, carrying their babies and their possessions on their backs. But now, they walked—no, they ran and skipped and jumped—out of Egypt with that new feeling in their hearts and in their heads. God would finally take them to their own land, where they could be their own masters.

But something stood between them and their new life, and that thing was the Red Sea. Old women sat still on the shore, staring out at the very, very wide expanse of water. Children lay with their heads in their parents' laps, their playfulness drained out of them at the sight of the lazy waves that almost seemed to be laughing at them.

Sitting there, they gradually felt another new feeling. There was a steady thrumming feeling that started in their chests and pushed its way through their bodies, right down their arms and legs, all the way to every fingertip and toenail.

Stronger and stronger it rocked, like an earthquake. The ground was shaking beneath their feet with the thunder of horses' hooves—thousands of horses' hooves—pounding toward them. Then they saw Pharaoh's army riding after them to bring them back to slavery. What they felt now was fear, shaking and quaking them to their bones.

Now God said to Moses, "What are you waiting for? *Do* something! Lead the Israelites on!" Moses looked ahead and saw the sea. He looked behind and saw the tips of soldiers' helmets just over the horizon. How could he possibly lead the Children of Israel anywhere?

He looked toward the circle of tribal leaders arguing by the shore. "We just need to go forward. Then God will save us," said one. His voice sounded strong, but his legs trembled still further into the sand. "Exactly," said another bravely, "and my tribe, being the bravest, will go first." But he didn't move, either. "No, my tribe will have the honor," said a third. His voice was shaking with the pounding, pounding, pounding of hoofbeats.

And so while all the leaders were bravely arguing, standing still nonetheless, a man named Nachshon walked right up to the water's edge. Slowly, he walked into the waves and looked right and left. The Israelites fell silent, watching. "Well," he called over his shoulder, "I don't know about all of you, but I believe that God is taking us back to the Promised Land. And if God says go, I'm going, sea or no sea." The thrumming was so loud that he could feel it in the water that was swirling gently around his ankles. He walked further, until the water lapped at the tops of his shoulders. From under the water, a school of tiny fish circled him curiously. When he turned to look at the huddled Israelites on the shore, they looked just as surprised as the fish. The pounding was now so loud that he could feel the waves of sound combining with the waves that licked at his earlobes. He walked into the sea until water leaked into his mouth, even further until water breathed into his nose, even further until he could see nothing but seaweed and sand whirling on the floor of the sea.

Then, although no one would have thought it possible, there came a sound louder than the hoofbeats. A sharp crackle and crash of waves pounded, not on the shore, but side to side, climbing on themselves higher and higher, as if in a rush to clear a path right down the center of the sea. The wind from the fleeing water whooshed so strongly that Nachshon felt his clothes drying stiff against his back. This time, when he looked to the left and then to the right, he saw walls

even more enormous than the walls of the pyramids he had sweated to build. These walls were made of water, flowing upward and crashing against each other. This time, when he looked back toward the shore, he smiled as if to say, "Here, I've found the way!" But no one would have heard him. The sounds of the Israelites shouting for joy would have drowned him out.

❧ 32 ❧

The New Moon

aron was out of breath when he reached his sister's tent. "Miriam," he said, "I need the women's jewelry."

She was expecting this. "What for?" she asked evenly.

"It's not for me," he said. "You know the people want to build a Golden Calf. *I'm* not going to start praying to idols, but the men—"

"You want *them* to pray to idols?" Miriam asked, raising her eyebrows.

"Well, no, of course not," he answered, "but the men need something, anything, to calm themselves. They can't wait much longer for Moses to come back. They're beginning to lose hope."

"And a Golden Calf will give them hope?" Miriam said.

Aaron sighed, exasperated. "Miriam, please. I just need to give them something to do until Moses comes back. Then they will see all their worries were for nothing."

"Well, I won't do it," she said and crossed her arms firmly. "And you shouldn't, either."

"All right, then, *you* come up with a better plan," Aaron said. "If you're so smart, what do *you* think we should do?"

"We should wait," Miriam said simply. "If our brother Moses promised to come back in forty days, then he will come back in forty days. But he has not been gone for that long."

"Maybe the men have lost track of time," Aaron said, his voice rising. "Can you blame them? The sun beats down on us all day, and the nights are black. They're tired and scared. I'm sure the women are, too."

"Tired, maybe, but not scared," she answered. "They wait and watch the skies and count the days and have faith—just as you should do."

Miriam knew that the women were tired—tired of the men continually asking for their jewelry. Every day there were new stories of women who refused to give their gold and silver to make this Golden Calf. One man took his daughter's bracelets while she slept, but the next day, she snuck into his tent and retrieved them. An old woman pretended she did not hear very well when asked for her earrings. Wives told their husbands that their wedding rings had gotten lost. It didn't matter how determined the men were, because the women could be determined, too.

And Miriam was sure the women were not afraid, even though the nights were indeed getting darker and darker. Instead, they looked forward to the darkening skies, because that meant the new moon was coming, and when the new moon returned, Moses would return, too. Here in the wilderness, after the children were asleep, the women would lie in circles, with their heads close together and their feet pointing outward, like the stars they were watching. Lying that way, staring up at the vast black sky, they would talk and tell stories. They would sing lullabies and shoo away nightmares. And they would inhale the clean air until they were lulled to sleep by the sound of tents flapping in the wind. When the nights were darkest, the new moon always returned. It had been that way since the beginning of time, and it would be that way forever.

And so, the Golden Calf was made without their help. The Israelite women continued to wait for Moses, until he returned, on the fortieth day, just as he had said he would. He brought with him two huge stone tablets, carved with God's laws. And his face was shining with joy—until he saw the Golden Calf.

Everyone cried when Moses threw the stone tablets to the ground, shattering them. They cried because they were sorry and because they were afraid. Even Miriam, for the first time, was afraid—afraid that God would never forgive the Children of Israel for making an idol, afraid that God would no longer want to be their God, afraid that God would never give them the laws that would make them a free people.

It seemed hopeless. Miriam threw her head back, eyes closed, to catch her breath. When she opened her eyes, she found herself looking right at the moon above. It was the narrowest possible sliver, but it was there, and it was shining steadily. Watching it, she felt steady, too. All the women who had come before her

had not lost hope—not four hundred years ago in Egypt and not yesterday in the heat of the desert—and she would not lose hope, either. She took a deep breath and headed for the tent of her brother Moses.

No one knows what they spoke about. No one knows whether she cried or pleaded or reasoned with him. Did she remind him of the women's faithfulness, or of all the years of slavery, or of the promises God had made to their ancestor, Abraham? Even Aaron couldn't guess. Perhaps remembering how he'd fought with Miriam about building the Golden Calf, Aaron simply smiled and said that if anyone could think of an argument that would change God's mind, it was his sister.

But we know this: After talking to Miriam, Moses did return to Mount Sinai. While he was gone, the people waited—patiently, this time—hoping against hope for God's forgiveness. They knew they had received it when they saw Moses returning, clutching another set of stone tablets.

And we know this: God gave the Israelite women an extra gift, a holiday every month, at the time of each new moon. Since then, women have watched for the new moon and celebrated its arrival. When the sky is darkest, they remember their unshakable faith in God. When the moon returns, they remember being given a second chance. And at each new moon, their hearts are filled with joy.

❧ 33 ❧

The Spies

Ten spies ran back to the Israelite camp, kicking up a cloud of dust on the horizon. Curious crowds greeted them, calling, "Yigal, please, tell us something!" and "What did you see, Palti?" and "We waited so long for you to come back, Ammiel. Don't keep us in suspense any longer!" But the spies had nothing to say, even to their leader, Moses. Breathless, silent, eyes on the ground, the ten men headed for their own tents. There, they threw themselves into the waiting arms of their families and cried.

But there was more dust on the horizon as the last of the spies, Caleb and Joshua, arrived. They carried a pole between them, and hanging from it were huge clusters of fruit. The two men were covered with sweat, their feet dragged through the dust with exhaustion, but they laughed loudly, their faces aglow.

"Moses!" cried Joshua, hugging him. Caleb spun his children around and kissed his wife. Joshua ignored the surprised faces and subdued voices all around him. He caught his breath and announced, "Children of Israel! We spies have returned from scouting the land that God promised to us. Our new home is beautiful, and the land is so good that . . . well, it's practically flowing with milk and honey! Just look at the fruit Caleb and I brought back. These grapes are huge, aren't they? And these pomegranates and figs—look at the size of them! Why, one of these figs alone could feed my family for a week! Try some of—"

"Beautiful?" cried Gaddiel, another of the spies. Tears still streaked his cheeks, and his forehead creased with disbelief. "Did we spy on the same land? How can you stand there and babble on about fruit! When are you going to tell them the rest of the story? Why do you hide the truth?"

"This *is* the truth," Caleb said, showing his hands sticky with grape juice. "They can see for themselves how rich the land must be to produce fruit like this."

"Then tell them *why* the land bears such big fruit!" Nahbi shouted as he pushed his way through the crowd. He stopped in front of Joshua and Caleb, staring hard at them. "Let me tell the people what you two have somehow forgotten to mention." He paused. "The fruit is gigantic because it has to feed—*giants*!"

The crowd drew its breath in.

"That's right, giants," called Gaddiel, as he, too, moved into the center of the crowd. "The people of this land must be huge! The sun probably looks like an ornament around their necks."

"It's true!" the spy named Shammua yelled from the other side. "They must be fierce! That land will swallow us whole!"

Over the crowd's muttering, Caleb had to raise his voice to be heard. "You don't know that! Why would Moses tell us that God wants us to conquer this land if it's impossible? Yes, their cities are large, but you're exaggerating."

"Exaggerating?" Shammua retorted. "Hardly. In fact, we would probably be surrounded by giant warriors. The Anakites on one side, and—"

"Amalekites!" shouted all the other spies. "Hittites!" "Jebusites!" "Amorites!" "Canaanites!"

"Listen to me!" Caleb barked. "If God says this land should be ours, we should go up right now and take it for our own. With God's help, we can defeat any enemy."

"Defeat them?" cried Ammiel. "We are like—like *grasshoppers* compared to them!" The people in the crowd gasped again. Their heads swiveled from man to man as they followed the spies' argument. On the one hand, there was that luscious fruit. On the other hand, maybe the land was the home of fierce giants. But on the other hand, Moses had said that God would be with them. But on the other hand. . . .

As if reading their minds, Caleb said, "Can't you trust Moses, you stubborn people? If Moses says that God wants us to—"

"Why should we listen to Moses?" the spy called Shaphat asked with a smirk. "What has he ever done for us?"

There was a shocked silence. Moses dropped his head into his hands, unable to speak.

Joshua stepped forward, nodding as if in agreement. "You are so right, my friend," he said. "Who does Moses think he is, ordering us around? Let's see if I can remember anything worthwhile about that man. . . ." Joshua tapped his lips with one finger as he thought. "Well, he was awfully nice about standing up to Pharaoh in Egypt and telling him to let us slaves go. We *were* slaves—remember?" Shaphat stared sullenly back at Joshua.

"And leading us out of Egypt," Joshua continued brightly. "Splitting the Red Sea so we could escape on dry land—remember?" Now all the spies looked at one another uneasily.

"Oh, and there is *one* other thing," Joshua said, snapping his fingers. "Moses went up to Mount Sinai to receive the Ten Commandments from God! Surely you remember that!" Joshua looked from spy to spy, daring any of them to argue with him. No one did.

"Now, *why* did God have Moses free us from slavery, and split the Red Sea, and bring us the Ten Commandments? To let us wander forever in the desert? No. To let us suffer defeat at the hands of some local warlords? No." Joshua paused again, feeling the strength returning to his tired arms and legs. His voice rang out: "We have come this far to return to our own land, the land God promised to Abraham, Isaac, and Jacob, and to Sarah, Rebekah, Rachel, and Leah. And to us, the children of their children—remember? That is our destiny. All we have to do is be brave, and it will be ours."

But as Joshua looked at the faces around him, he did not see bravery. He saw fear and confusion and the stubbornness of slaves. It would take time for the Children of Israel to learn how to be brave, to learn how to be free. Joshua's first battle would be for the hearts and minds of his own people. Only then could they conquer the land they had been promised. Joshua would have to wait.

Many years later, Joshua did lead the Israelites triumphantly into their new land, and they found it to be like no other place in the world. It was a land of hills and valleys, a land of great variety—from the snowy mountains in the north to the blazing desert in the south. It was a land surrounded by seven seas and four rivers. Three friends holding hands could not reach all the way around carob trees— that's how thick their trunks were. Olive trees yielded their oil like springs. Cinnamon was so plentiful it was used to feed goats! Grapes grew in clusters as big as oxen. It really was a land flowing with milk and honey, so beautiful that all the nations of the world wished to have it for their own. And it was a land that the Children of Israel would have to fight to win, over and over again.

❧ 34 ❧

Rabbi Shimon's Cave

himon bar Yochai and his son sat across from each other on the floor of their cave. They were supposed to be eating lunch, but Rabbi Shimon, as always, was studying.

"Carob stick?" Eleazar asked, breaking the long silence.

"No, thank you," his father answered.

Eleazar let a moment pass. "Mashed carob?"

"No, thank you," his father answered.

"Some carob juice, then?" Eleazar couldn't help smiling.

Rabbi Shimon looked annoyed. "Don't try to be funny, Eleazar. Has it occurred to you that maybe I too miss eating something other than *carob*, day in and day out for *eleven years*?"

"But father, don't you think the emperor might have forgiven you by now?" Eleazar asked. "Can't we can go home? I miss mother. I miss home. I miss food!"

"I know, son," Rabbi Shimon said quietly. "But no one speaks out against the Roman Empire and goes unpunished. God gave us this safe place to hide, this carob tree, even a spring of water. Without these miracles, we wouldn't be alive today! So I will continue to devote my life to being grateful and praying and studying, for as long as God grants me the privilege of doing so. And you should be grateful, too!"

Rabbi Shimon paused to catch his breath. And then, he added, more gently, "Now, son, let's not talk like this any more. It's time to rest and be glad. We still have a drop of wine left to greet Shabbat. And, after all, what is Shabbat without wine?" He smiled for the first time in a long time.

And so they spent their days eating carob, praying, studying in the mornings, and telling stories at night. Only once a year did they receive visitors, when Rabbi Shimon's students came, disguised as hunters, although the only thing they were really hunting for was learning. While the students drank in Rabbi Shimon's wisdom, Eleazar devoured the wine and bread they had brought along. And even more than food, he hungered for news of the outside world. But not his father. Apart from asking about his own family, Rabbi Shimon did not seem to care a bit about the rest of the world. If something did not concern study or prayer, to him it simply did not exist.

One morning, while it was still dark, Eleazar was startled out of his sleep by the sound of footsteps. It couldn't be the students back so soon, could it?

"Father, did you hear that?" Eleazar whispered.

Rabbi Shimon nodded. "Who's there?" he called nervously.

But there was no answer. The footsteps stopped at the edge of the cave. Finally, an old man stepped inside and spoke.

"I've come to tell Shimon bar Yochai that the emperor is dead," the man said in a deep voice. "You are free to leave this cave and return home."

Eleazar stared at the man for a moment. Then, he jumped up from under his blanket and began to sing and dance for joy.

His father, however, did not move. "Who are you?" he asked.

"Someday, you will know," the man said simply. Then, he turned on his heel and disappeared.

Eleazar was ready to leave the cave that instant, but Rabbi Shimon did not rush. First, he said his prayers. Then, he packed up his holy books and a bit of carob. Finally, he took his first steps outside the cave in eleven years. At first, it was all too much: the blinding sun, the wide-open spaces, even the gentle whistling of the birds was more than he could bear. While Eleazar ran ahead, picking wild berries, his father held tight to his little bag of carob. Despite his own delight at being out of the cave, Eleazar soon saw that everything here was a distraction and a bother to his father. Even the farmers lying idly in the fields, laughing and eating lunch, annoyed him.

"Look at them, Eleazar," Rabbi Shimon grumbled. "This is how they choose to use their freedom! Thinking only about feeding their bellies. They care nothing about feeding their minds! Why, they could be spending their days studying God's holy words, and they wouldn't even have to hide in a cave to do it!"

"Perhaps they would, if only God sent them carob, too," Eleazar answered with a laugh. "But then who would grow food for all the rest of the people?" His father did not seem to hear him. Rabbi Shimon walked on, looking disapprovingly at everyone, from the shepherds resting by a well to the merchants on their way to market. The more he saw, the angrier he got, until it seemed that his look alone would set the world on fire.

Just then, the old man appeared on the road in front of them and spoke harshly in his deep voice. "It seems that Shimon bar Yochai is *not* ready to leave his cave after all! He needs to remember how to appreciate everything that God created. He needs to return to his cave for another year and study—study how to live in *this* world!"

Now, it was Eleazar's turn to be the teacher, while his father was the student. For the next year, there was much to teach. He brought Rabbi Shimon figs and dates so that his father could learn to savor the tastes he had forgotten. After they stood on a nearby hillside to watch sheep grazing, Eleazar brought a blanket made of their wool back to the cave to keep his father warm. And every Friday, Eleazar bought wine in the nearest village, so that they could properly welcome Shabbat.

Finally, it was time to try to leave the cave again. As they set out, Rabbi Shimon took a deep breath of fresh air. This time, he praised the trees, the farms, and the animals on the way. This time, he stopped to talk to the same laughing farmers out in the field. "You, there," Rabbi Shimon called to them, "what are you working at, please? Tell me how this makes you so happy."

The men looked up, startled. "We're harvesting, of course," one of them answered, holding out a big cluster of sun-warmed, purple grapes. "Who wouldn't be happy with grapes like these?"

"And don't forget," the other farmer added, "when they get turned into wine, they will make you even happier!" And both farmers started laughing again.

As Rabbi Shimon bit into one of the grapes, a smile spread slowly across his lips. "That's right," he told Eleazar. "And what is Shabbat without wine?"

⚘ 35 ⚘

The Crack in the Diamond

The king sat on his throne, admiring his diamond ring. When he turned it this way and that, it was like light itself exploding and scattering everywhere. This was by far the most precious, perfect jewel in the kingdom.

The only thing more precious to the king was his son, the little prince whose smile was almost as dazzling as the ring he would one day inherit along with his father's throne. So when the boy clamored to wear the ring himself, it was very hard to say no.

"Little one," the king said instead, "this is not a toy. This is not to play with." The king tried to gather up the child, who was now whimpering and clinging to his father's leg.

"Don't be sad," the king said. "I'll give you something else to play with. Here, take my crown."

But the little boy, wailing louder than before, batted the golden crown away as if it were a bug.

"But, dearest one," the king tried, "this ring is very fragile, very delicate. We must be very careful with it."

The boy's tears quit as abruptly as they had started. "Careful? I will be careful." He nodded seriously, locking his father in an irresistible gaze, as only a two-year-old can.

While his father was deciding whether to argue or laugh, the boy wrenched the ring from the king's finger, pressed it to his chest, and ran away yelling, "It's mine! Mine! *My* ring!" between peals of laughter.

Well, there is really no point in telling what happened next. Let's just say that when the boy returned—looking very sorry indeed—there was a crack in the diamond. A flaw on the king's perfect diamond! The royal ring ruined!

Fix it? Impossible! One cannot fix a diamond as if it were a broken plate.

Replace it? Impossible! One cannot replace a diamond as if it were a stained shirt.

Wear it anyway? Impossible! One cannot wear a diamond if it is not absolutely perfect.

But what is impossible for you or me is not impossible for a king. "If I command that it be made perfect," the king proclaimed, "so shall it be!"

The servants of the palace brought the ring from jeweler to jeweler. When they first saw it, the finest craftsmen in the city would exclaim, "It is gorgeous, marvelous!" When they looked more closely, they would moan, "It is hopeless, useless. The diamond is cracked, and nothing can make it perfect."

But in a little jeweler's shop at the end of a twisting alley, in the old Jewish Quarter of the king's capital city, there was someone who disagreed. This someone was a jeweler who examined the ring and said simply, "Of course, I can make it perfect."

"But how can you?" the servants demanded. "Every other jeweler in the land has said it is impossible."

"There is nothing—no problem—no matter how big or small, that cannot be fixed," the jeweler answered. "Besides, what makes something perfect? It's all in how you look at it."

Well! the servants whispered among themselves. Who does this jeweler think he is? How arrogant! Boasting that he can fix that diamond when every master craftsman in the kingdom knows it's impossible!

But an order is an order, and so the servants brought the jeweler before the king.

"Is this the one who claims he can fix my ring?" the king asked, eyeing him suspiciously.

"It is, Sire," one of the servants answered. "Of course, he's probably lying. Should we send him to prison now?"

"Of course not, you fools!" said the king, waving them away. "We'll give him a chance to fail first."

As the servants led the jeweler away to the royal workshop, the king called after him, "Just remember, it must be nothing short of perfect!"

The jeweler nodded pleasantly, the guards closed the workshop door behind him, and everyone settled down to wait.

The jeweler worked all day and into the night without stopping. Finally, the guards peeked inside. "He's just stalling," they grumbled to each other. "There's nothing he can do to fix that ring. A crack is a crack. It's ruined!"

Just then, the jeweler opened the workroom door, handed the guards the royal jewel box, and told them he was finished.

"I'll say you're finished," the guards laughed. "When the king sees that the ring is still ruined, it's off to prison with you!"

"Oh, I don't think so," the jeweler answered as they escorted him to the king's throne room. "Not only did I fix the ring, I made it better! As I always say, there's nothing that can't be fixed. It's all in how you look at it!"

The king was waiting. The little prince was wiggling impatiently on his knee.

The guards bowed and presented the royal jewel box. "Your Majesty," they announced, "your ring."

"Ring?" yelped the boy. "Ring, daddy, ring! Give me mine ring!" In a flash, he was sliding off his father's lap and heading straight for the ring.

"Oh, no, you don't!" said the king, leaping up to follow him. "That's how we got into trouble in the first place."

But by then, the boy had grabbed the jewel box and flung it open. He tossed the box on the floor and held the ring up to his face. "I will be careful, I will be careful," he repeated under his breath. His eyes opened wide and yelled, "It's a flower, Daddy! A flower! *My* flower!"

The king finally caught up with his son, just in time to see what so delighted him.

On the face of the great diamond, the jeweler had etched an exquisite, tiny design. It was a rose, so perfectly rendered that it looked real. Each facet of the gem held another delicately unfolding petal. And the jeweler had transformed the ugly, jagged crack into the flower's sturdy stem.

The King's eyes shone in the reflected light of his precious diamond. It was fixed. It was even better than before. It was perfect.

❧ 36 ❧

The Two Sisters

It was a quiet night. The wind blew softly through the trees, and the moon cast its bluish light on two houses cuddled next to each other. Tova's house was silent except for the gentle breathing of her children, all tucked in together like peas in a pod. Bracha's house was quieter still. And yet, if you listened very closely, you could make out the distinct sounds of worrying coming from inside both of them.

Tova turned over in bed again and fussed with her blanket. How tired her sister Bracha had seemed today as they worked side by side in their field. "Poor thing!" thought Tova. "Bracha works so hard at harvest time, and she doesn't even have any children to help her. Maybe I could do more for her. Oh, but she's so stubborn! She would never ask her big sister for help."

Bracha, too, was wide awake and worrying, but not about any troubles of her own. No, it was just that Tova was looking so tired today. "Poor thing!" thought Bracha. "She works so hard at harvest time, and she has so many little ones to care for. Why, with only half of our harvest, she has to feed her whole family. Maybe I could do more for her. Oh, but she's so stubborn! She would never ask her little sister for help."

Tova couldn't bear to lie in bed another minute. The more she thought about her sister, the more she felt the unfairness of it all. "At the end of the day, at least I can come home to my beautiful family. But Bracha—what does she have to come home to? An empty house. No wonder she looks so tired. I have so much, and she has so little. I have to make things right."

At exactly that moment, Bracha sat straight up in bed. "How could I have been

· 151 ·

so selfish all these years? After a hard day of work, I can come home, relax, and enjoy the peace and quiet. But Tova—what does she have? A husband and a house full of children all clamoring for her attention. No wonder she looks so tired. I have so much, and she has so little. I have to make things right."

So Bracha ran outside, to the side of her house, where she stored her grain in sacks. "Just as I suspected—I have much more than I need. It's only right to give Tova half of mine," she thought as she rolled up her sleeves and set to work.

At the side of *her* house, Tova had just come to the same conclusion. "Just as I suspected—I have much more than I need. It's only right to give Bracha half of mine," she thought as she rolled up *her* sleeves and set to work.

Tova dragged bag after bag of her own grain past the front of their houses as quietly as she could. After she put one bag on her sister's pile, she raced back to get another. As she rubbed her aching arms, she noticed that there still seemed to be as many bags in her pile as ever. No matter how fast she dragged them to Bracha's side, Tova felt like she'd never be done!

That's because *Bracha* was dragging bag after bag of grain past the *back* of their houses as quietly as *she* could. After she put one bag on her sister's pile, she raced back to get another. This is going to take a lot longer than I thought, Bracha realized as she threw another sack against the side of Tova's house.

As she stood there, catching her breath, something bumped into her, knocking her face-first into the pile of sacks.

"Ooof!" a familiar voice groaned. It was Tova, who had also toppled to the ground and lay in the dirt next to her. "Bracha, what are you doing here?"

"What am *I* doing here? What are *you* doing here?" Bracha demanded, as she took Tova's outstretched hand. The sisters pulled each other back up to standing.

"You've been bringing me some of your grain, haven't you?" Tova said in her big-sister voice.

"Well, yes, but—" Bracha began.

"But I've been doing the same thing for you!" Tova said, grabbing both her sister's hands in her own and leading her to the side of the other house.

Bracha started giggling first. "No wonder it seemed to take forever to move a few bags of grain! Every time I brought one of my bags to your side—"

Tova interrupted. "—I was bringing one of mine to yours. We could have gone on all night!"

"I just wanted to help you," Bracha said. "I thought you needed it."

"Not at all," Tova answered, hugging her close. "If I have you, I already have everything I need."

The love in that hug was so great that even God could feel it. This was the kind of hug that God remembers forever. And that is why, many years later, Solomon built his magnificent Temple on the very spot where Bracha and Tova stood that night. God wanted the Holy of Holies to stand right there, on the place where two sisters loved each other even more than they loved themselves.

✣ 37 ✣

The Five-Shekel Thief

Along the coast of the Mediterranean Sea, there once nestled a tiny village, no bigger than a dot on the map. The whitewashed houses were topped by rust-colored tile roofs, and brilliant splashes of flowers overflowed windowboxes. Doors stayed open day and night to catch the warm breeze, which flowed easily from house to house. The people of the village were as gentle as the weather, uncommonly good-natured and honest. Yes, it was an absolutely perfect place to live. That is, until Mendel came to town.

You see, Mendel was a thief. Well, let's not be rude. It's not nice to call people names. Let's just say Mendel sometimes took things without asking first.

You can imagine the changes in the village after Mendel arrived. Doors were shut tight during the day and locked as night fell, and windows were shuttered closed. Jewelry was kept hidden out of sight, and people started carrying all their money in snug little bags hung around their necks.

But though the villagers were now more guarded about their belongings, their hearts were still open. Mendel never lacked for a holiday invitation, and children waited outside anxiously until he arrived. It was easy to be nice to him because—apart from his being a you-know-what—he was so charming and amiable. Mendel would tell some silly stories, find a coin behind a giggling little girl's ear, and lead everyone loudly in a few songs. And then, as the evening was drawing to a close, his hosts would count the silverware, rescue their candlesticks or wedding rings from his pockets, and send him on his way. Mendel didn't mind this routine either, because, after all, he knew he was a—well, you know.

At first, Mendel found that all this kindness made his job difficult. But it did-

n't stop him, and his stealing got worse and worse. Finally, the town leaders decided to ask the rabbi for help.

Soon after, the rabbi went to visit him. Mendel was honored but surprised. He had never had such a distinguished visitor before! He quickly offered the old man a seat and produced some almonds and pistachios, which had somehow fallen into his pocket—with only a little help—at the market the day before. Then Mendel poured some coffee and slowly stirred sugar into it with a neighbor's silver teaspoon. The rabbi said thank you, shaking his head a little sadly as he recognized his own carpet beneath his feet.

"Mendel," he said gently, "we have to talk. I hear you need a job, and I need someone to help me take care of the synagogue. If you come and work for me, maybe I can teach you some Torah while you earn some honest—er, well-deserved—money."

Mendel looked bewildered. "Work for a living? Me? Is it possible?"

"Sure," said the rabbi. "You would have to keep the synagogue clean and tidy. And you would have to polish the golden menorah, the silver crowns on the Torah, the *tzedakah* box. . . ."

"But is it a good idea for me to handle such valuable objects?" asked Mendel doubtfully.

"Of course it is," said the rabbi. "All you need is to learn a little Torah and to have some responsibility. I'm sure you will show us what a good man you really are. So come by at about. . . ." The rabbi reached into his pocket to check the time, but his watch was gone.

"Sorry," Mendel said, as he returned it with an impish grin. "It's a habit. I'll be there in an hour."

So that is how Mendel the Thief became the shammes of the synagogue.

The rabbi knew that Mendel had never been to school, so he decided to teach him as they worked together. On that first morning, the rabbi put him right to work washing the windows and polishing the woodwork. "I want everything to sparkle for Shavuot, the holiday that's coming in a few days," he explained to Mendel, who was standing on a ladder with a rag in each hand. When they brought in armloads of flowers to decorate the synagogue and a layer of sweet-smelling grass to spread over the floor, the rabbi told him, "All these holiday decorations remind us of how the Children of Israel stood at the foot of Mount Sinai to receive the Torah." The rabbi even found a way to turn lunchtime into a lesson. He invited Mendel to eat at his house, where his wife was busy preparing cheese pastries and honey cake, "because the Torah is like milk and honey," he said. Mendel listened to all these explanations with his eyes wide with wonder.

The next morning, he was scrubbing the floors when the rabbi called to him, "When you're ready for a rest, look up at the plaque of the Ten Commandments. That's what God gave the Jewish people at Mount Sinai, and that's why we celebrate Shavuot." Knowing that Mendel could barely read, the Rabbi helped him slowly sound out all the words, paying special attention to the ones that said, "You Shall Not Steal."

Mendel looked at those words for a long time, his scrub brush dripping soapy water on his shoes. Finally, he said, "That's a lot of rules. How will I remember them all?"

The rabbi clasped him by the shoulders and said, "A very great scholar named Akiva once said that the whole Torah could be summed up this way: 'Love others the way you love yourself.' That's all you need to know to be a better person." Mendel seemed cheered by this and, nodding vigorously, went back to his work.

Actually, the rabbi was impressed with Mendel's progress. He was learning quickly, the synagogue was spotless, and nothing was missing!

"Mendel, I'm very proud of you," the rabbi told him on the third day. "You've learned a lot in a short time, and I can see that you have really changed. Before you go home tonight, let's count all the donations that the villagers have given for Shavuot. Tomorrow, we will give the money to people who need it. Then you'll learn how much better it feels to give than to take." He paused and looked right into Mendel's eyes. "And just in case you're tempted to take any of it, we'll put the money right here, under the words 'You Shall Not Steal'—just to be safe." Mendel nodded.

At the end of the day, the rabbi put the ten shekels they'd counted from the *tzedakah* box under the Ten Commandments, and the two men left to go home.

The next day, Mendel was late to work at the synagogue. "Did I make a mistake by trusting him?" the rabbi wondered, his heartbeat quickening. He went to Mendel's house, but it was completely empty. Not a stick of furniture, not a pot or pan, not his carpet—nothing remained. Mendel had packed up and run away— but why? Suddenly, the rabbi remembered the donation box. He burst into a run, entered the synagogue, found the box, and, fingers trembling, opened it.

Inside were only five shekels and a note that was smudged and dotted with crossed-out words. It was from Mendel.

"Dear Rabbi," the note read. "Last night, I couldn't stop thinking about all that money, and I was really tempted to take it and run away. But when I came to the synagogue to get it, I saw 'You Shall Not Steal,' and I remembered what you taught me. Rabbi, you will be very proud of me, because I restrained myself and decided to take nothing! But then I remembered how Akiva said, 'Love others the way you love yourself,' and it was clear what I should do! So I left five shekels for my neighbors and kept five for myself. And you were right. I feel like a much better person now!"

The rabbi sighed. "Well," he thought, his face brightening, "it's a start."

❧ 38 ❧

Dear God

Shmuel had to put together a Friday-night meal somehow, but all he had in his bag so far were a couple of sardines and a carrot. Up ahead was the fruit stand, though. Perhaps, if he asked nicely, Moishe the Fruit Seller wouldn't mind giving him a few of the bruised apples, the way he usually did.

"Here comes 'Shmool the Fool,' expecting us to give away our merchandise again, no doubt," Moishe was saying suspiciously. "Well, not me. Not this time."

"You shouldn't talk that way," Rayzel the Baker chided. "Shmuel, come over here," she called. "I have a challah for you. It's a little lopsided, and I don't think it was baked all the way through. But it's yours if you want it." She dropped the misshapen challah in Shmuel's bag and pushed him along before he could even say thank you.

"Well, if you ask me," Moishe retorted, "we should all stop giving him charity! Shmuel has a job. Shmuel has no children to provide for. So why does he come around here begging every week? He must spend his money foolishly."

"He's not a bad person, he's just not too bright," Rayzel said, as if Shmuel weren't standing right there in front of them. "He trusts that God will provide."

"God? You say *God* will provide?" Moishe said, shaking his head. "It seems to me that *we've* been doing the providing. But that's a good idea. Next time, let Shmuel ask God for help. *I* still have to earn a living!"

With those voices still ringing in his head, Shmuel trudged home to his little shack at the top of the hill. He found himself walking more and more slowly as he thought. Maybe his neighbors were right. *Had* he been taking advantage of their charity? Maybe he *should* ask God for help!

He burst into a run, his sad old bag flapping against one leg. The moment he got home, he found a nubby pencil and scrap of paper and sat down at his bare kitchen table. His stomach grumbled expectantly. "Don't worry, tummy," he said, patting his middle, "you won't be hungry for long."

He began to write. "Dear God," his letter said. "I was wondering if, perhaps, You might help me, Your humble servant, Shmuel. As usual, I am running out of money. I just don't know where it all goes. So I am turning to You for help. Maybe You could teach me to manage my money a little better. Meanwhile, if You can send me some food, my stomach and all the vendors at the market would be very grateful." He signed it, "Shmool the Fool."

Then he went back outside. When he felt a strong gust of wind, he let go of the letter and watched the paper float away. Then he hurried inside to welcome Shabbat with his feast of sardines and half-baked challah.

But the wind did not take his letter to God. Instead, the letter skimmed along the hilltop like a dove. It flew over houses and through trees. It flew over valleys and hills, past gardens and lakes, until finally it landed in the palace courtyard.

In fact, the letter fell right at the feet of the queen herself. She read the letter over and over. "Imagine!" she thought, wiping away tears. "Imagine that a message from such a faithful soul should land right at my feet. It must be a sign from God telling me to help this poor man." The queen commanded her servants to take a wagon filled with food and wine and clothes and coins to Shmuel's house. "And make sure no one sees you," the queen warned them, "for this is an act of charity commanded by God!"

One blustery night about a month later, Shmuel was awakened by an insistent knock at the door of his shack. It was a weary traveler, asking for a place to rest. Shmuel was too busy bustling about, poking the fire and bringing an extra blanket, to notice that, in spite of her dusty clothes, his guest had a noble air. This guest was the queen herself, who, out of curiosity, had disguised herself to find out whether her charity had helped "Shmool the Fool."

The queen's eyes darted about eagerly. But the more she saw, the more disappointed her expression grew. Where were the precious clothes, the fine wine? Why, there was no sign of her gift at all. There didn't even seem to be much food in the pantry.

Then the queen spied one of her own wine goblets on the mantel. "Say, isn't that a wonderful goblet!" the queen said.

"Oh, yes," answered Shmuel, smiling a little. "It came from God."

"Really?" said the queen, leaning forward expectantly. "How so?" Finally, she would discover where the rest of her charity had gone.

"Well," said Shmuel, sitting down with a sigh, "I once asked God for help, and the next thing you know, a great treasure was sitting on my doorstep. Enough to last a lifetime. If only. . . ."

"If only what?" the queen prodded.

"If only I hadn't gone and spent it—the way I always do!" Shmuel shook his head miserably. "The food went to the children at the orphanage. And the wine went to the *shul*, of course. The clothes went to the dowry fund for poor brides. There were coins, too . . . oh, the roof at the school needed to be fixed. Hmm, what else? You see, I've already lost track of it all! But it doesn't matter, because the treasure is gone. All except for this goblet," he said, cradling it tenderly in his hands. "I'm saving it as a reminder of God's kindness to me. But I don't deserve it. I didn't change. It's true what everyone says. I'm just as foolish as ever."

The queen said nothing. The next morning, however, when she returned to the palace, she helped to load a wagon with food and wine and clothes and coins. She instructed her servants to bring the wagon to the little shack on the hilltop, and to deliver another one just like it to Shmuel every month, forever.

Deborah Lights the Way

Lappidot squinched up his face as he read very slowly: "The fat cat sat on the . . . fl . . . flat mat? Fat mat?"

"Flat," said his wife, Deborah, looking over his shoulder. "That was right. Go on."

"The dogs . . . jog in the . . . fog bog?" Lappidot wiped a bead of sweat from the side of his forehead. "Frog bog!"

Deborah squeezed his hand. "You're really making progress," she said. "Soon, you'll be reading like a whirlwind across the desert." In the dim candlelight, she thought she could see him smile.

But his voice was tired when he answered. "Deborah, I know you mean well, but I don't think I'll ever learn to read." She opened her mouth, but he was not done. "Really, I can hardly remember the alphabet. A grown man sweating over 'frog bog'—it's humiliating! I'm just not smart enough to learn."

Deborah's first thought was to argue with her husband. But part of being wise is knowing when to be quiet, and she was very wise indeed. Deborah was a scholar. She spent her mornings studying, and her afternoons studying some more. At night, she would write poetry until her candles burned out.

While Deborah the thinker lived inside her mind, Lappidot the farmer lived in his fields. His only studies came from the earth that he worked. His knowledge of soil and crops and weather was so vast that he could have written volumes about them, that is, if he knew how to write. But, of course, he couldn't write any more than he could read, even with the wise Deborah as his teacher.

"I think you are just as smart as the smartest scholar in Shiloh," she told him.

She stared up at the ceiling, as she always did when a poem was taking shape. "You are a scholar of the land."

"Oh, Deborah, stop trying to make me feel better," Lappidot laughed. "Who am I? An ignorant farmer. What can I offer? Grains, vegetables!" He held out his hands so she could see the dirt under his fingernails.

Deborah found it hard to sleep that night. She wanted to convince Lappidot that he was smart, in a different way than she was, but smart all the same. It seemed impossible. When the candle on the table began to sputter, she reluctantly blew it out. What work could one do in the dark, after all? Suddenly, she sat up straighter. An idea had come to her, fully formed, and it did not involve poetry, or arguments, or even words. Wide awake with excitement, she began to work.

All night, Deborah made candles, as she often did for the house of study in Shiloh. But these were no ordinary candles. These wicks were twice as thick as usual, twisted so tightly that the candles would burn for hours. The layers of wax were perfectly flat. Deborah was concentrating so hard that she was surprised to notice the sun coming up. But when she and Lappidot lugged their baskets of candles to the house of study in Shiloh, she did not feel tired at all.

The scholars there looked pleased when they saw Lappidot and Deborah arriving. "Look here," exclaimed one of the men, reaching into a basket. "Deborah understands the kind of candles scholars need! With wicks like these, we can study all night. Thank you!"

Lappidot blushed with pride. "Thank *me*?" he laughed. "You mean Deborah."

"No, I mean both of you," said the man, offering Lappidot a seat at a huge table spread with bread, cheese, yogurt, and sturdy bowls of fruit.

"Quite right," said another scholar, thoughtfully nibbling a fig. "Farmers are like Deborah's candles, Lappidot," he said, nodding in her direction. "Your food lets us study, just the way her candles do, you see."

"After all, who can learn on an empty stomach?" said the first man, as he handed Lappidot some bread. "I'm sure you've heard the saying, 'Without bread, there is no Torah.' "

Lappidot looked up, only to find that Deborah was already grinning at him.

"Although we can never repay you for your hard work," another scholar at the table was saying, "we would be honored to try."

"You know," Lappidot answered, "it's funny you should offer, because there *is* something you can do for me."

The sun was high overhead and the road was shimmering with heat when the couple returned home from Shiloh. Deborah happily swung her empty baskets back and forth with each step. Lappidot walked jauntily at her side, his head high. In a loud voice bursting with feeling, he was singing the alphabet song. Maybe he would never be a scholar, but he was doing his best, and that was enough.

Years later, Deborah became a judge who led Israel. Some assumed that God had rewarded her so richly because she was a wise woman—a teacher, a scholar, a poet. Others thought perhaps it was because God knew she could do anything—settle disputes, advise generals, or lead armies into battle. Only Deborah guessed at the truth: that God rewarded her for understanding that each person shines with a unique light.

❧ 40 ❧

The Best Weapon

D avid looked around and strained to see through the darkness of the cave where he was hiding. He gasped again and again, trying to catch his breath, as his heart pounded. How could it have come to this? How could it be that King Saul, who once loved him like a father, was now forcing him to run for his life? David leaned against the damp cave wall and, still panting hard, closed his eyes.

David thought back to Saul's proud face when he had returned from fighting Goliath, so long ago. "Hooray for David, who saved us from the wicked Philistines!" the crowds called out. "Hooray for the only one brave enough to fight the giant!" they cheered as they carried him, victorious, back to Saul's palace, where the king had proudly hugged him.

After that victory, Saul taught David how to be a real soldier, and David was a good student. The king had laughed with pleasure when he heard the women of the palace chanting a little song whenever David returned from battle: "Saul has won his thousand battles, and David his tens of thousands."

David sat at the king's side every night, playing the harp for him, just as he had done years ago, when he was nothing more than a shepherd boy. When David's music rang out joyfully, Saul threw back his head and sang along. And when Saul's mood turned quiet, the tunes became thoughtful. More and more, though, his moods turned angry. Then, David played only the most gentle, soothing music to calm Saul's fury. But it was no use. Saul's anger and sadness flooded the palace, and David's music didn't seem to help.

Many times, the king would lash out at everyone around him for no reason at all. Saul's anger was terrifying, and when he heard that little tune—"Saul has won his thousand battles, and David his tens of thousands!"—his face grew tight, and the veins in his neck bulged. "You're trying to steal the throne from me, admit it!" Saul would suddenly scream, although there was no one else in the room. Once, he even threw a spear across the throne room, aiming at an enemy only he could see.

"Saul has won his thousand battles, and David his tens of thousands!" Over and over again, those words buzzed in Saul's ears like troublesome mosquitoes. As time passed, his pride in David turned to jealousy. Jealousy soon turned to anger, and anger turned to hatred. Then the hatred grew bigger and bigger, until King Saul could think of nothing else. It grew until it was bigger than Goliath. It grew so big that neither Saul nor David could fight it any longer.

Now, as he leaned against the cave wall, sweaty and exhausted, a real voice from outside the cave interrupted David's memories. Instantly, his eyes blinked open, and every muscle in his body tightened. Surely the voice belonged to one of Saul's soldiers.

David saw that it was Saul himself, though not the king whom David had once known. This Saul was growling like a wild animal and cursed furiously as he entered the cave. David held his breath, afraid that Saul would discover him at any moment. But Saul's eyes were not used to the dark inside, and he never saw David crouching in the shadows. Still muttering angrily, the king curled up on the floor of the cave, exhausted from his search. A few moments later, David heard the soft, steady breathing of a man asleep.

David's whole body sagged with relief. He crept out from hiding and bent over Saul. David heard only his own thoughts. "Attack Saul now, while you have the chance!" he told himself. "If you don't kill him now, you'll be running away from him for the rest of your life!"

So David knelt down, pulled out his dagger, and stared at Saul's face. Asleep, Saul looked like the man David had always known, the man he loved like a father. His eyes clouded with tears, David clutched his dagger more tightly. Then, very slowly and carefully, David cut the hem from King Saul's purple robe, crept back into the shadows, and waited.

When Saul woke up, he immediately stumbled out of the cave, as if he was eager to continue the hunt. David watched him for a moment, then burst out of the cave and called, "Saul, King of Israel, it is I, David!"

Saul spun around. The look of surprise on his face erupted into a strange, cruel smile. "Why do you run from me, David?" Saul asked. He spoke softly, but his hand was reaching for the hilt of his sword.

"Because I know you want to kill me," David said simply. "But you are still my king, and to prove my loyalty to you, I spared your life today."

"Spared my life?" Saul retorted. "Such arrogance! How could you spare *my* life? You have been running from *me* all day!" And he began to draw his sword out of its scabbard.

"Then how did I get this?" asked David, holding out the hem he had cut from Saul's robe.

Saul's eyes snapped downward. When he saw the cut in his robe—exactly the size and shape of the cloth David held in his hand—he stared back at David in confusion. David had had the chance to kill his most bitter enemy, but instead, he had let Saul live.

Saul's fiery eyes filled with tears, and his rage and wildness drained away. In front of him stood David, the sweet boy who had lulled him to sleep with his harp, the warrior who had won yet another battle with no weapon but himself. And before Saul could stop himself, he threw down his sword and hugged David, the next king of Israel.

⁕ 41 ⁕

The King and the Worm

enaiah, come and look over these plans. They're magnificent, don't you think?" King Solomon beckoned his friend toward a massive pile of drawings.

"Thirty cubits high, sixty cubits long, and twenty cubits deep! This is huge!" Benaiah said, shaking his head in amazement.

"Exactly," said Solomon happily. "I knew you'd love it."

Benaiah had watched Solomon's ideas for building the Temple grow more complicated and grandiose with every passing day. Now he had to bring him back down to earth. "Solomon," he began in the lecturing tone he often had to use, "I really feel—considering the trouble we're facing with this project—it would be problematic . . . uh, no, im-*poss*-ible to, ah. . . ."

But Solomon had already wandered off to the other end of his throne room. "Benaiah!" Solomon shouted. "Where are you? I've been waiting ages to sing you this new song of mine!"

Benaiah crossed his arms stiffly. "I've been right here, trying to tell you—"

"Oh, sorry," replied Solomon, abashed. "Well, no matter. Listen to this." But the moment he opened his mouth to sing, a completely different thought poured out. "Hmm, let me jot this down first," he said, tossing bits of parchment over his shoulder as he searched for something to write with. "I've just had the most wonderful idea for a new throne. What if it were made of ivory. . . ."

"Ivory?" Benaiah murmured weakly. When Solomon was in one of these creative moods, there was no point in getting in the way.

"Yes, ivory, and stop interrupting," Solomon snapped. "Let's say there will be six steps leading up to the seat. I want lions on each side." He paused. "Did I say lions? No, wait, not just lions, but tigers and eagles, too. And here's the best part!" Solomon's eyes popped open, as if his brain could not contain the wonders of his imagination. "We'll install a mechanism inside, so when my foot touches the first step, the lion on the right will reach out its paw, while on my left, the ox will stretch out its leg, and so on. As I ascend my throne, different animals will help me up to the top. And then, when I sit down, an eagle will place the crown right on my head! What do you think?"

"Solomon, it's great, but—"

"The whole throne will be overlaid in gold. With vines and palms for a canopy. And linen, painted with pictures of lightning and fire. And rainbows."

"Sol—"

"Please! I'm not done!" Solomon said, looking injured at his friend's interruptions. "I want bells hanging from the canopy so that a breeze will make them jingle. And I want a large golden lion to be filled with fragrance, and—"

"Solomon!" Benaiah finally shouted, directly into the King's face. "The *Temple!* You promised to build God's Temple! Remember?"

Solomon just rolled his eyes, but at least he stopped talking.

Benaiah took a deep breath, waiting to make sure Solomon was really finished. "Everything is ready," he began, ticking off supplies on the fingers of one hand. "Hiram of Tyre has brought all the cedar from Lebanon that you asked for. The olive wood and cypress are ready, too. The stone is here, the skilled workers are here, everything's ready." Benaiah's voice trailed off, and he smiled a weary smile. "Once you solve our one teeny tiny little problem. . . ."

Benaiah knew he was being cruel, for the problem was anything but tiny. God had decreed that the Holy Temple be built in Jerusalem—a building of peace in the city of peace. That meant it could not be created using materials of war. *That* meant no metal—no hammers, no chisels, no drills to cut and shape the stone. And *that* meant the only way that the great King Solomon could build his majestic Temple was with the help of a teeny tiny little . . . *worm.*

That's right, a worm! A worm called the *shamir,* no bigger than your little fingernail, but more powerful than a mountain. God had created this miraculous worm to do only one thing—to eat through solid rock. And to do it for only one purpose—to build the Holy Temple. And to do it for only one man—the great Solomon, who ruled in peace.

But the *shamir* was guarded day and night by a fierce eagle who drove away anyone who approached her hiding place, high in the hills around Jerusalem. If God wanted Solomon to build the Temple, why make it so difficult? If God wanted Solomon to use the *shamir*, why keep it just out of his reach? Solomon loved riddles, but this one was no fun. Benaiah watched his old friend rub the bridge of his nose anxiously, just as he did every time he was reminded of the riddle of the *shamir*.

So Benaiah said gently, "Solomon, enough thinking. Let's just go have a look at this guardian eagle. Maybe a plan for capturing the *shamir* will come to you."

The next morning, before the sun came up, the two men climbed the mossy hillside and hid themselves near the cave of the great eagle. They watched as the stealthy bird flew to and fro, bringing food to her babies nested in the protected cave. She watched over her little ones with pride, looking around vigilantly while they ate.

Solomon sighed. "I know," Benaiah whispered to him sympathetically. "Even if we find where this bird is hiding the *shamir*, she'll never let us have it. Just look at the way she tends to her babies. Why, she'll do anything for them. She's ferocious!"

"That's it!" Solomon suddenly hissed. "Come on! What's taking you so long?"

"Huh? For what?" Benaiah whispered back. "What are we doing?"

"We're going to make that eagle *need* to show us where the *shamir* is!" Solomon announced, darting ahead. He pointed to a huge boulder and motioned for Benaiah to help him push it. Together, arm muscles bulging, they forced the boulder forward until it covered the mouth of the eagle's cave. They could hear the squawking of the startled baby birds inside the cave as they scrambled back to their hiding place.

A few moments later, the giant bird was back. She circled the cave a few times, confused. Why were her little ones trapped behind this rock? The babies inside squealed frantically. Desperately, she pecked at the rock and scraped at it with her talons, but it did no good. Finally, she reached into her own wing feathers with her beak and delicately pulled out something so small they could hardly see it. Solomon clutched Benaiah's arm tightly, for he knew it must be the *shamir*!

A moment later, there was no doubt at all. The mother eagle placed the bright white speck on the boulder, which began to crumble apart, falling away from the cave opening. While the mother eagle hopped through the rubble in search of her

babies, Benaiah crept soundlessly toward the rock. Trembling, he picked up the *shamir* and placed it in Solomon's cupped hands. For a long moment, the two men stared at the tiny creature. Then they stared at each other. Without a word, they ran down the hillside in a cloud of dust.

Seven years later, Benaiah climbed up the same hill to watch Solomon supervise the finishing touches of the Temple. He was proud of his old friend's accomplishment, of course. But something pleased Benaiah even more, and that was the thought of Solomon—powerful, rich, grand, and creative—struggling to get a tiny worm.

❧ 42 ❧

What the Baker Forgot

Nate leaned over the six-tier wedding cake he was decorating, his face scrunched up with concentration. *Flower, swag, flower, swag, dot-dot-dot* went his hands, smoothly squeezing the icing bag this way and that. "Yes," he thought, nodding to the awestruck crowd that stood watching outside his shop window, "this is my best work yet. I'll probably become famous for this!"

A gasp of horror broke into his thoughts. The people outside had noticed—although he had not—his sleeve accidentally brushing against the icing. "Such a masterpiece, ruined!" murmured the crowd. But Nate merely shrugged and turned the smudge into a bouquet of perfect sugar roses. The crowd broke into relieved applause, and Nate bowed in every direction, completely unaware that a giant dollop of pink frosting graced the end of his nose. But the crowd did not laugh; no, Nate was an artist of frosting, a professor of custard, a genius of yeast! A man like that could not be expected to care about whether there was flour in his hair or frosting on his nose.

One night he came home very late, as usual, and collapsed into bed next to his wife. "Nate," Elisa said sleepily, "will you be home for dinner Friday night?"

"Can't, my little cupcake," he answered. "Too much to do. First, there's all those carrot cakes, then the . . ."—*yawn*—" . . . apple tarts, then. . . ." A pause, then—*snore*.

The next morning, before the sun came up, Nate was already hard at work, sprinkling cinnamon over some sticky buns. There was a sharp *tap-tap* at the shop's door, which startled Nate so much that he dropped the canister of cinnamon, sending a cloud of fragrant spice into the air and all over his face. A girl from the neighborhood stood outside the door. "Oh, sorry! I didn't mean to bother you!" she said as Nate opened the door, sneezing and coughing. "I was just wondering if you had challah for sale."

"No challah," Nate replied, brushing cinnamon out of his eyebrows. "Sorry."

But after he closed the door behind her, the word "challah" settled into his mind like powdered sugar on a doughnut. He could almost taste the delicious challah he used to bake with his mother. The crust was golden, firm but not hard, and the inside was so eggy that it seemed more cake than bread. Suddenly, Nate was filled with such longing that he decided to make a few loaves right away.

The yeast was bubbly, the flour as smooth as silk, the loaves artistically braided. But when they came out of the oven, Nate could see that they looked different from the challah of his memory. And when the loaves cooled, he could taste that they were not the same, either. This challah wasn't bad, exactly. It just didn't match the bread he remembered from so long ago, the bread that his mother kept hidden under the gold-embroidered challah cover on the Shabbat table. It seemed to take forever for her to light the candles, and the *Kiddush* his father sang went on and on. Then, it was time to pull away that cover, revealing the proud, braided loaves waiting patiently for their own blessing. Nate said the *Motzi* himself, and then—and then, finally, he could bite into a sweet, chewy morsel. Oh, such perfect deliciousness was worth waiting for!

Nate realized that he had been standing in the middle of his bakery for a long time, drooling. "How embarrassing," he thought, wiping his mouth. "And to make it worse, I can't even remember the simple recipe for my mother's challah. It would have been so good for business!"

As he tumbled into bed late that night, he meant to tell Elisa that he had been trying to make his mother's challah. But he was so tired that he could barely open his mouth to talk. "Elisa," he mumbled, his eyes already shut, "sweetie pie, what about challah?"

"What's that, dear?" his wife answered. "Challah? I think there's still some left over." But Nate—*yawn, snore*—had already fallen asleep.

For the next few days, he could think of nothing but challah. Every morning, he woke up kneading his pillow in anticipation. At breakfast, he sprinkled poppy seeds on his cereal. And all day long, he baked nothing but challah: big challah, small challah, round challah, braided challah, poppy-seed challah, sesame-seed challah, challah with raisins.

By Friday, every table, every shelf was filled from floor to ceiling with challah. In the middle of the bakery sat Nate, absentmindedly braiding his own beard and lost in thought, wondering why none of the challah seemed quite right. He was so deep in concentration that the sharp *tap-tap* at the door made him jump off his stool in a panic, upsetting a dozen eggs in the process.

It was the little girl from the neighborhood again. Her face brightened when she saw the huge collection of challahs. Nate stepped aside, wiping up the mess while she made her choice. She inspected the loaves, one by one, squeezing and sniffing and poking. But instead of picking one, she turned to Nate and asked sadly, "Have you run out of your mother's challah already?"

"Did you say my mother's challah?" Nate asked, grimacing as he pulled eggshells out of his shoelaces. "How do you even *know* about it?"

"My family had Shabbat dinner with yours a few weeks ago," the girl said. "The challah was so delicious! Your wife said she made it from your mother's recipe, so of course I thought I could buy some in your bakery." She looked around, shaking her head. "You have a lot of nice things here, but they're not what I'm looking for. I want what your family has every week at home!"

Late that afternoon, Nate closed his shop early. When he arrived home, he opened the door cautiously and peered in. Elisa was blessing the children, whose faces gleamed in the light of the Shabbat candles. The table was set with the prettiest dishes and a silver cup of wine. But Nate's eye was drawn immediately to the gold-embroidered cloth that covered a platter in the middle. Before he could say hello, before he could even stop himself, he rushed to the table, yanked off the cover, and saw—his mother's challah!

"This is it!" he cried. "It's just right!"

The children, surprised to see their father, rushed to hug him. Elisa kissed her husband with a bemused smile on her face. "Yes, Nate, it is just right," she said. "But you're a little too early for the *Motzi*."

"Elisa, how can this be?" Nate said, smoothing the challah cover back over the golden loaves and tumbling weakly into a chair. "I've been trying and trying to make my mother's challah, but I just couldn't do it. And here it is in my own home!"

"Don't you remember?" said Elisa. "When we were first married, your mother gave me the recipe, and the children and I make challah every week." She ruffled his hair, dislodging a few chocolate chips. "You've been so busy with the bakery

that you're never home to celebrate with us, but Shabbat has been here all along."

For the first time in years, Nate enjoyed a Friday night with his family. He sang the *Kiddush*. He *really* tasted his food. He cuddled with his children. He talked quietly with Elisa after dinner. His worries melted away with the candles. Finally, feeling completely relaxed, he fell asleep in his chair. When Elisa roused him to go to bed for the night, he was startled, until he remembered that he didn't need to do anything or go anywhere. A day of rest was beginning, and everything he needed was right there at home.

❦ 43 ❦

Solomon and the Miser

O ne for you, two for me. One for you, *three* for me." Bavsi was bent over his desk, counting coins and doling out pay to his workers.

"Step aside, let the next one through," called Bavsi impatiently. "One for you— Wait, what am I doing?" he said, shaking his head and frowning. "No, no, no! I take it all back. There will be no more money given today! Go away! Away, do you hear me?"

One of the workers in line spoke up nervously. "But, sir, this is not charity you're giving us. This is our pay. You owe it to us!"

"You are quite right," smirked Bavsi with a nasty grin. "But if you are *not* my workers, then I don't have to pay you. So you're all fired!"

Bavsi was the richest man in town. Unfortunately, he was also the meanest and stingiest man in town. He was so mean and stingy that he was famous for it. It was said that he went to bed at sunset so that he wouldn't have to buy candles, that he kept his house so cold in the winter that you could see your breath indoors, and that he never married or had children because it would cost too much to feed them! And now he had dismissed all his workers so that he wouldn't have to pay them.

It was hard to be surprised by any stories about Bavsi, but no one—no one— could believe the latest gossip.

Now, this was a terrible time in Israel, when there had been very little rain, crops had grown poorly, and everywhere people were hungry. The richest families opened their storehouses and distributed food to the poor. But not Bavsi. Instead of sharing his grain, he was selling it, and at a very high price.

Every day, a long line of hungry people would gather in front of his door, some spending their last coins, others hoping, by some miracle, that Bavsi would take pity on them. But, of course, he had no use for beggars.

"Give you some food?" he sneered one day at a poor woman and her daughter. "I'm a businessman. I'm not here to *give* you anything. Now, if you want to *buy* some food. . . ." So the woman slowly slipped the wedding ring from her finger to pay for some grain while Bavsi tossed half a scoop of it into her bucket.

The little girl hoisted her mother's bucket off the table and trudged back toward the door. As she waited for her mother, a dusty brown sparrow landed beside her.

"You are just like me, little sparrow, always looking for something to eat," she told the bird in a tired voice. "But at least you don't have to beg from Bavsi." She took a few bits of grain and offered them to the sparrow, who gratefully nibbled right from the palm of her hand. "I bet if Bavsi could be hungry for just one day, he wouldn't be so mean," said the girl, as she tossed one last crumb at the sparrow's feet. The bird eagerly continued to eat as he watched the girl hurry off with her mother. Then he smoothed his feathers and flew straight to King Solomon's palace.

Now, everyone knows that Solomon could understand animals, but few people know that he could also speak with the birds. The little sparrow flew right to the throne room to tell the king all about the girl, and the ring, and the grain, and Bavsi.

Solomon listened intently as the little bird pipped and squeaked. Every once in a while, the king would interrupt with a "No!" or a "How terrible!" Finally, the sparrow ended his story and flew off, wings flapping furiously. Solomon stared after him, tapping his chin with one finger.

The next day, King Solomon ordered his royal chef to prepare a feast. "But Your Highness," stammered the chef, "how can you entertain at a time like this?"

"Oh, this food will not be wasted, I assure you," said the king. "You'll see."

When Bavsi received an invitation bearing the royal seal, he read it over and over. "Finally, I am getting the honor I deserve," he announced loudly to the hungry crowd assembled outside his door. "It's about time the king invited me to dinner. Why, I'm probably the richest man in the kingdom—maybe richer than Solomon himself!" Bavsi's forehead creased. "Perhaps the king wants to borrow money from *me*," he thought with alarm. But his worry was quickly replaced by greedy excitement.

Bavsi skipped breakfast and lunch that day, so that he would be able to take full advantage of the king's hospitality. By the time Bavsi arrived at the palace, his mouth was watering just thinking about the exquisite delights to come. A chamberlain led him to the banquet hall to wait for the king and announced, "In order to dine with the king, you must follow three rules: First, when the king asks if you are enjoying yourself, you must be lavish in your praise. Second, you must not request anything. And third, you must not ask any questions." Bavsi, too hungry to care, just nodded vigorously and demanded, "When do we eat?"

"Ah, ah, ah! Remember what I told you about asking questions!" the chamberlain scolded. "Wait here for the king's arrival." He left the room, leaving ajar the door to the palace kitchen, where Bavsi could see and smell the preparations for the feast.

After what seemed like two or three hours, King Solomon swept into the banquet hall. Bavsi's stomach was growling, and he felt a little faint as he sat at the table. He could barely answer the king's polite questions about the weather without drooling.

The first course was soup, steaming fragrantly from a golden tureen. Bavsi tucked a napkin under his chin and was already lifting his spoon expectantly. A servant placed an enormous bowl in front of him.

"Tell me," said the king suddenly, "are you enjoying the meal?"

Remembering the chamberlain's first rule, Bavsi answered, "Oh, Your Majesty, it is the finest meal imaginable. The linen—it is magnificent! These, uh, spoons—they are works of art!" Solomon glowed with pleasure at the praise. Then, just as Bavsi was finally about to dip his spoon into his bowl, a servant appeared at his side and whisked it away. Bad luck! thought Bavsi. From now on, I won't talk so much.

Next, silver platters of roast chicken were carried into the hall. The aroma of the golden-brown pieces encircled the table. This time, when Bavsi's plate was placed before him, he was ready to pounce.

Just then, the king asked, "How is everything? Need any salt?"

"Salt?" said Bavsi. "No, no, I'm sure it is perfectly seasoned, thank you!" But before he could take a breath, a servant cleared his plate away again. He opened

his mouth to ask for it back, but he remembered the chamberlain's second rule and said nothing.

Bavsi strained to keep up with King Solomon's pleasant conversation while the vegetables and salad and dessert all made the briefest of appearances in front of him before being snatched away. After dinner, drinks were served but not drunk. Stories were told but not heard. Finally, after a midnight mint not tasted, King Solomon offered Bavsi an invitation to spend the night. And a royal invitation could not be refused.

As the long night passed in a sumptuous palace bedroom, poor Bavsi could think of nothing but food. His head ached, and his stomach made the most wretched growling sounds. The tears that rolled down his cheeks were the first thing he had tasted since yesterday's dinner.

Why had he been treated in this way? He knew he couldn't even ask; that was the chamberlain's third rule. But he had all night to think about it. It finally occurred to him that his troubles had started when he received Solomon's invitation and that he had been invited to this unbearable evening only because he was so rich. Suddenly, Bavsi had a great urge to give all his money to charity.

The next morning, the king seemed greatly amused to hear that Bavsi had left the palace before sunrise. "He didn't even stay for breakfast!" said Solomon with a little laugh. "Well, a man like that must be very busy."

And so he was. In front of Bavsi's house stood the usual long line of people, but on this particular morning, they all received heaping buckets of grain from his very own hands. In fact, when the little girl and her mother approached, Bavsi patted the child gently on the shoulder as he urged the woman to take two buckets of grain instead of one.

Long after the famine had ended, people remained mystified about Bavsi's new enthusiasm for charity. He was so eager to give away every bit of his fortune that he even coaxed the neighborhood birds into his yard by tossing handfuls of crumbs there every day. A little brown sparrow would sometimes interrupt his meal to tell his friends the story of what happened to Bavsi at Solomon's palace. As for Bavsi, he was pleased just to know that a poor man like him would never again be invited to a royal feast.

⸎ 44 ⸎

The Gift of Tears

hy? Why did I do it?" Eve wondered aloud as she sat by the edge of a brook, watching the water flow over the rocks. But the brook had no answer for her.

So she laid her head down and watched the setting sun. And again she asked, "Why? Why did I do it?" Instead of answering her, the sun just sank beneath the horizon, taking with it Eve's last rays of happiness on her final day in the Garden of Eden.

As the sky turned from blue to darkest black, Eve asked the stars, "Why? Why did I do it? Why did I take a bite from that fruit? I wasn't even hungry!" But the stars had no answer, either.

God had given Adam and Eve only one rule for living in the Garden of Eden: Don't eat the fruit of the Tree of Knowledge. But that is exactly what they had done. Now, they would have to leave the Garden of Eden, this perfect place, forever.

She watched Adam staring up into the night sky and knew he had no answers. They both had been curious about the Tree of Knowledge for some time. "Why doesn't God want us to have knowledge?" they had asked each other. "What secrets is that Tree keeping from us?" But they had never dared to eat any of its fruit—until now.

"Why?" Eve burst out. They could have had any other fruit they wanted! She didn't even feel more knowledgeable.

Adam merely shook his head in response.

Eve and Adam spent the rest of the day in silence. It hurt too much to talk, and there really wasn't anything to say. They just waited for God to tell them it was time to leave paradise, to show them what life would be like outside the Garden.

By afternoon, Eve's heart ached with grief as the gates of Paradise began to open. She and Adam said silent good-byes to the plants and the trees and the flowers. They blew kisses to the birds and the animals. At the Garden's gates, they turned to take one last look behind them.

"I'm so sorry," said Eve. "If only we could undo what we did."

"If only we could change the past," said Adam, holding her hand.

Eve closed her eyes and inhaled the perfumed air one last time. "If only we didn't have to go," she said. "If only this moment could last forever."

But the time had come, and the gates of Paradise were closing behind them. As they took their first steps into the world outside the Garden, they heard God's voice speaking to them softly.

"You ate from the Tree of Knowledge," God said, "and now there is much you will know. You will know fear, and you will know sadness—but you will also know surprise and joy. For the first time, you will know pain and hard work—but that means you will also know the excitement of dreaming and the delight of accomplishment. You will know good times and bad. There will be times when life seems too hard, and for those times, I am giving you something that will help."

"Is it something from Paradise?" asked Eve.

"A tree, or a fruit, or a rainbow?" asked Adam.

"No," answered God, "it is not from Paradise, but it will help you remember. This gift will come from yourselves. Whenever you are feeling sorrow—the way you feel now—whenever the pain gets too hard to bear, whenever you are truly sorry or frightened or lonely, I will give you tears, so that you can cry. And though tears are not from the Garden of Eden, they will lighten your hearts and give you a glimpse of Paradise again."

Eve turned to Adam and saw that tears were already running down his cheeks. Her own cheeks burned hot, and when she touched her eyes, they felt wet. Her tears turned to sobs, and finally her whole body shook as she cried.

Memories of their days in the Garden flowed as freely as her tears. The peaceful animals, the wondrous flower petals, the glorious sunlight. Then came memories of their curiosity, and the Tree, and the fruit she had eaten. Eve's tears flowed on and on.

There were more images—this time of the future. Eve could see herself carrying a baby as she worked in her own garden. She saw Adam turning soil and harvesting vegetables. She saw visions of homes built and people gathering to eat and drink and celebrate. She felt the comfort of a good night's sleep after a hard day's work.

When Eve opened her eyes, everything seemed clearer and sharper. Her body still throbbed with sorrow, but that terrible pain in her heart had eased, and her head felt lighter.

Eve turned to see that the gates of the Garden of Eden had closed. She saw Adam drying his tears with the back of one hand. When he looked up, his face, too, shone with a new kind of peace.

Ever since that day, people have found comfort in tears. Although both bitter and sweet, tears are a little taste of Paradise.

❖ 45 ❖

Rachel's Testimony

Once there dawned a day so sad that even the angels cried. Even Abraham, Isaac, and Jacob cried. Even Sarah, Rebekah, Leah, and Rachel cried. Even the Torah and all twenty-two letters of the alphabet gathered to share in the sorrow.

The Jewish people had lost the last battle in a long war. The victors had left the land of Israel ruined, spoiled the beautiful Temple that Solomon had built, and filled it with idols. The Jews were forced to leave their homeland and go to faraway countries as exiles or slaves.

Abraham looked out over the Temple Mount, which was in ruins, and tears rolled down his face. When he saw that dogs were roaming the Holy of Holies—a place so sacred that only the High Priest had been allowed to enter—his sadness turned to anger. He raised his face and cried out, "Creator of the world, how could You do this?"

"It was not I who did this, Abraham," God answered him. "The Jewish people—your very own descendants—did this to themselves. They turned their backs on Me and started praying to idols again! They turned their backs on the Torah. They even turned their backs on the twenty-two letters with which it was written!"

Abraham raised his chin defiantly. If the Jewish people were his children, then he would defend them, as if he were a lawyer in a courtroom. "If they are guilty," he said, his voice rising, "then show me proof. Show me witnesses who will testify against them."

God—knowing that it was only Abraham's sorrow that made him speak this way—said softly, "The Torah itself can testify."

After a few moments, the Torah stepped forward and looked around nervously. Abraham was not gentle as he began his questioning. "How dare you!" he began in a boiling whisper. "How dare you come here today and say that my children rejected you? In fact, they were the only nation in the world to accept you! They embraced you without asking a single question, without asking for anything." Then he stared at the Torah and demanded, "Are you really going to be a witness against the Jewish people on their day of greatest sadness?"

The Torah, looking only at the ground, withdrew in silence.

God spoke again. "If the Torah will not testify, then bring in the twenty-two letters of the *alef-bet*, and hear what they have to say."

"Alef, how can you testify against my children?" said Abraham, whirling around to confront the first letter. "Have you forgotten that you begin the Ten Commandments, that you are the first letter in *Anochi*—'I am the Eternal One, your God.' Don't you remember that my children accepted those commandments on Mount Sinai when no other nation would?" Then, even before Alef could answer, Abraham turned on his heel to face the second letter.

"And what about you, Bet? Aren't you the first letter in the Torah? *B'reishit*—'In the Beginning' begins with you! Have you forgotten how even the youngest of my children loved to read and study, beginning with you?" Bet burst out sobbing and ran away, and all the other letters followed.

Abraham turned to God and said proudly, "You see? No one will testify against my children." He paused to catch his breath. In a different, lower voice, he added, "Remember that I left my home to travel to a distant land merely because You told me to. You promised to make my name great and my children numerous. Please, for my sake, have mercy on those children and bring them back from their exile today." But there was no answer. Abraham sat down, exhausted.

In his place, Moses stepped forward to reason with God. "Master of the universe," he began, "I left the comfort of Pharaoh's palace to be a faithful shepherd to the Children of Israel. For forty years, I guided them when they wandered in the desert. And after all that, You wouldn't even let me enter the Land of Israel. I didn't argue then, but now"— Moses's chin puckered with emotion—"won't You please have mercy on Your children today, for my sake?" But only silence followed.

Next, Rebekah called to God in a firm voice. "If You won't listen to him, what about me? Didn't I willingly leave my family to marry a man I had never met, all because I trusted in You? Please, for my sake, have mercy on Your children." Still there was no answer from God.

Jacob rushed forward. "What about me?" he burst out. "Didn't I work twenty years in order to marry Leah and then Rachel? Didn't I risk everything to return to Canaan? We raised our children with such care—with such love! And now all our work lies in ruins—now it is all for nothing!" When he fell to his knees, crying bitterly, the silence that followed seemed impossible to bear.

Finally, Rachel came forward. She touched Jacob's arm tenderly, took his upturned face in her hands, and dried his tears with her fingertips. "Dear God," she said quietly, "You know how dearly Jacob and I loved each other. You know that he was tricked into marrying my older sister, Leah, before he could marry me." Here she had to pause, and the hands that she used to wipe her face were still wet with Jacob's tears. When she spoke again, though, her voice was steady. "I did not let jealousy get the best of me—I who am nothing more than a human being. So how could You, all-powerful God, be jealous of mere idols and allow Your children to be punished because of them?"

Rachel's words rang clearly and sharply with the rightness of her argument.

At last, God spoke. "Cry no more. Yes, the Temple is destroyed, and the Children of Israel have been sent away. But for your sake, Rachel, I promise that your children will return to their home. I promise that they will rebuild the Temple. I promise that everything will be right again—someday."

❧ 46 ❧

A Match Made in Heaven

How about Menachem, the prince of Acco? I'm told his family is very wealthy and their land is. . . ." King Solomon searched his daughter's blank stare for some sign of interest, but he found none. He tried again. "Perhaps he could visit so you could get to know. . . ." His voice trailed off as he saw her roll her eyes, for he knew that, no matter how much he talked, the conversation was already over.

The truth was, Solomon was no more enthusiastic about this talk than Shira was. It wasn't that it was hard to find men willing to marry her. There were plenty of them; after all, Shira was wise, kind, and beautiful, not to mention the daughter of Solomon, the most powerful man alive.

The problem was Shira herself. Fine young men would come to call, expecting to find her in the palace library, perhaps, with her royal tutors. But no, Shira was never home. Burning with curiosity, Solomon sometimes followed her. One day he would find her at the marketplace bargaining with traders in languages that were foreign, even to him. Another day, she might be playing her flute in the meadow or, knee-deep in mud, watching villagers dig a well. It hardly mattered that sweat pasted her hair to the back of her neck. Always, she was radiant. When she spoke, everyone leaned toward her, like sunflowers, to bask in her warmth.

At times like these, Solomon—he who had built the glorious Temple in Jerusalem; he who had commanded the building of a cedar palace; he who had written songs and proverbs—that same Solomon would give up, let his head fall into his hands with a groan, and order his carriage back to the palace. It would not be easy to find a husband for someone like Shira. No, it would be impossible.

At the end of another frustrating day, King Solomon fell into bed and entered the world of dreams. At first, his dream was beautiful: Shira, his precious daughter, the shining jewel in his crown of achievement, was dressed as a bride. The *ketubah*—the gorgeously designed wedding contract—was signed. He was leading her proudly to the *chuppah*. But who was the groom awaiting her there? A poor man, dressed in rags—a peasant! Who could it be? Solomon spun around to find the groom's name on the *ketubah*, but the words wavered before his eyes. From the top of the document, though, one phrase shone boldly: the date of Shira's wedding was exactly one year from this very day.

He awoke, shivering. The vision was so clear, so vivid. It must have been a prophecy.

Before the sun had time to rise, he had already sent for Shira. "My dearest child, I have had a vision that you will marry a poor man . . ." Solomon began in a serious voice.

But Shira interrupted at once. "Oh, good, Father! I'm so tired of all these princes who care only about wealth and finery. Who is he? Can you find out whether he's musical or—"

"Did you hear what I just said, Shira? A poor man! You! It's impossible!" thundered Solomon.

A noise escaped Shira's throat. It sounded like the beginning of a laugh, but she bit her lip and said in a steady voice, "You're right, Father. I guess you'll have to give him enough money so he won't be poor anymore."

It seemed that Solomon would have to devise a plan on his own. At the end of the day, the king's advisers announced: A tower would be built on a small island in the middle of the sea. There, Shira would be locked—no, protected—for the next year. In that way, the terrible prophecy could not come true.

At first, Shira was shocked by her father's plan. Locked up alone in a tower, with only a few servants for company, for a year! But, then again . . . alone in her tower, she could catch up on her reading. Alone in her tower, she would not have to suffer through one more matchmaking dinner. Alone in her tower, she could play the flute night and day if she wished. And so, it was a very happy princess who waved good-bye from the tower's rooftop.

As soon as her father's boat was out of sight, though, all Shira's courage left her. And to make it worse, the sky darkened and the wind began to lash the trees back and forth. What storm could move in so quickly? As she turned, she saw that this was no storm approaching, but an enormous bird, a bird so large as to block out the sun, so swift as to make waves pound on the beach. Her father had told Shira legends of a monstrous bird called the Ziz, and now here it was, flying straight toward her!

The Ziz was covered with jet-black feathers, each one as big as she was. Its talons held the limp form of a man, and its eyes hunted for still more to eat. Her servants shrieked and pushed each other through the door into the tower. For a moment, Shira stood motionless. Then she pulled her flute from her sleeve and blasted three shrill notes. The Ziz must have been surprised by this fierce response, for it dropped the man right there on the tower roof, reared up, and with three beats of its vast wings flew out of sight.

Turning to look at the man, Shira saw that he was now sitting up, shaking his head back and forth. His clothes were shredded around the edges, like a banner that had been flying too long. "Thank you. You saved my life," he gasped. "I was out working in the fields when that creature came out of nowhere and snatched me up. How did you scare it away?"

"Oh, I learned that trick from some shepherds," said Shira, trying to sound calm, although she too was shaking.

He gestured at a small instrument tucked into his belt. "I, too, have a flute," he said. "I never had much, but now it is all I have left," he added with a rueful grin.

At dinner that night, Shira's servants snickered at this pathetic creature who had fallen from the sky. He was so busy stuffing food in his mouth that he could barely speak. It was just as well, they thought. What could they possibly have to talk about? Still, freshly bathed and dressed, he looked a lot better than when he had landed on the roof. Now they could see his face was open and handsome.

When the servants returned to refill the wine goblets, they found the two young people engaged in intense conversation. Shira was showing him some papers, he was nodding vigorously, and the sounds of lighthearted banter soon filled the little stone tower.

You may think that a wedding has to be fancy, with flowers and tall cakes, but when Shira and her young man decided to marry, right there on the top of the tower, it was a very simple affair. The days that followed flew by quickly.

But not for King Solomon. Exactly a year after his dreadful dream, he rushed to set sail for the little island, congratulating himself on having rescued Shira from the terrible prophecy of marrying a poor man.

"Father, Father!" called Shira, running down to the shoreline, "I have so much to tell you!"

But, there was no need for words. In her arms she carried a very little baby, and by her side was the handsome young man, whom she proudly introduced as her husband.

King Solomon's eyes darted back and forth, trying to make sense of it all. Shira had somehow managed to marry a poor man, in spite of all his careful planning! How could this have happened? In the silence, Shira placed the baby in her father's lap, and his face softened. As he gazed into the face of his new grandchild, the king suddenly knew the answer: When the heavens decree that two people are meant to be together, there is nothing—no king, no ocean, no Ziz—that can keep them apart.

❧ 47 ❧

The Wedding Present

rincess Pilar tried on her wedding gown once more and admired her
reflection in the mirror. The dress was exquisite, the veil just right. Even
her shoes were flawless.

"Perfect!" she sighed, pulling off her veil and tumbling onto her bed. "But
whom will I marry?"

From the sound of her voice, you might think that no one wanted to marry
Pilar. But the truth was that too many men wanted to marry her. And not just any
men, but three wonderful brothers, her favorite friends. They were handsome,
they were kind, and they were funny. To make it worse, she adored all three of
them. How would she ever be able to choose just one for a husband?

At first, she simply refused to decide. But, finally, the mere sight of that gorgeous wedding gown made her feel miserable, and she knew it was time to act.

Princess Pilar called the brothers to her side. "Dearest friends, I love all three
of you, and I know you all love me. I can't possibly choose one of you over the
other two. So, instead, I propose a contest."

The brothers looked at each other, intrigued, and nodded for her to continue.

"Each of you will go your own way, traveling to the far corners of the world,
and each will return in one year's time with a present for me," Pilar explained.
"Without knowing which gift belongs to which man, I will choose the present I
like best, and the giver of that present is the man I will marry. The contest will be
a fair one, so no matter who wins, we can all continue to be friends. Agreed?"

"Agreed!" the brothers said together. They kissed their beloved princess, shook
hands with each other, and set off for their separate adventures.

Exactly a year later, the brothers met on the outskirts of Pilar's kingdom, just as planned. They were tired from their long journeys, but still full of enthusiasm for the contest. They hugged each other joyfully and set out the presents they had found.

Rafael, the oldest, was first. "Dear brothers," he said, "you know I love you both, and I wish you the best of luck, but I'm afraid you're going to lose this contest. Look at what I found!" And he unrolled a tattered and stained carpet.

His younger brothers burst into laughter. "You think Pilar will like that old rag?" chortled Gabriel, the second brother.

"Actually, I do," said Rafael as he stepped onto the rug. "Just watch!" As he spoke, the carpet rose into the air and hovered just above the heads of the others. Rafael pointed here and there, and the carpet followed his commands, whirling him through the sky. Finally, he waved his hand with a flourish, and the carpet gently set him down.

"A magic carpet!" said Gabriel, applauding. "Very nice, very nice. I'm sorry to have to tell you, though, that my gift is even more wondrous!" From a velvet bag he pulled a small, tarnished mirror. Around the edge and down the handle were spaces where jewels had once sparkled, but they were long gone.

"An old mirror?" said Miguel, the youngest. "What's so special about that?"

"When you look into it," Gabriel said breathlessly, "you can see anything you want to, no matter how near or far it may be." He gently tapped the crackled glass, which immediately reflected their old parents sitting near their hearth at home, talking and drinking tea. The three men jostled each other for a good view, and Gabriel's eyes shone with pride in his gift.

"This *is* wondrous," said Miguel in a quiet voice. "All I brought was a leaf."

"A leaf?" cried Rafael, jerking away from the mirror.

"Little brother," said Gabriel, shaking his head, "what were you thinking?"

"Listen," Miguel said, "and then you'll understand." He cleared his throat. "I had traveled everywhere and found nothing to bring Pilar. I was in a faraway land, exhausted—and sad, too, for I knew it was almost time for us to meet. I was sitting under a gnarled tree with blue leaves, resting, when I noticed a mother bird teaching her babies to fly. One by one, she nudged them out of the nest. But the last one, the littlest one, was not quite ready. He flapped his wings a few times, but fell to the ground instead. He wasn't moving and seemed badly hurt. The mother bird snatched one of the blue leaves from the tree, flew down to her baby,

and pressed the leaf into its beak. In a moment, the baby bird hopped up, chirping happily, as if he had never been hurt! So I plucked a leaf from that tree and returned home as quickly as I could." Miguel pulled a tiny box from his sleeve and opened it. Inside was a flat, round leaf that glowed the color of the summer sky. Miguel paused, looking from Rafael's confused face to Gabriel's skeptical one. "I don't know," he said, shrugging. "I guess I was hoping it was . . . maybe some kind of magic healing leaf, but there's no way to try it without ruining it."

Rafael jumped up and hugged Miguel. "You never know, little brother," he said. "It's up to Pilar to decide, anyhow."

Gabriel patted Miguel's shoulder. "That's true," he agreed, "and to cheer you up, let's look into my mirror and see what she's doing." He held it up and tapped.

But when the three men again peered into the glass, they gasped with horror. The once-lovely Pilar lay in bed, looking very pale. Doctors paced around her bedside, and the king and queen sat nearby, crying. How could it be that Pilar—vigorous, playful Pilar—had become so sick?

"Quick!" cried Rafael. "Hop onto my carpet! We must go to her at once!"

In an instant, the carpet sped them across the kingdom and right into the window of Pilar's bedchamber. The princess's parents stared at the brothers, openmouthed, but Miguel ignored them and the crowd of royal doctors. He headed straight for Pilar's side and placed the leaf on her lips.

Not a sound was heard in the room. After a long moment, Pilar's mouth began to move. Pilar slowly chewed, and then her eyelids began to flutter. Finally, she sat up in bed, jiggled her legs over the side, and laughingly demanded to know why everyone was staring at her.

"She's well! She's well again!" cried her mother, the queen.

"Thank God your three friends returned at exactly the moment you needed them!" exclaimed her father, the king.

The room was filled with chattering as the brothers hugged Pilar, their old friend, while her parents cried tears of relief, and the royal doctors excitedly discussed the unexpected recovery.

Finally, everyone in the room became thoughtful and quiet, for the moment of Pilar's decision had arrived.

The queen held her daughter's hand as they considered the brothers' gifts: the magic mirror that had allowed them to see that she was in distress, the magic carpet that had flown them to her rescue, and the magic leaf that had cured her illness. "I can tell you no more than that, Pilar, dear," she said. "I'm afraid your contest has made it harder than ever for you to choose among them."

"No, Mother," Pilar answered, smiling, "I *have* chosen my husband. I will marry the brother who brought me the leaf."

Miguel barely had time to call out, "That was my gift!" when Rafael stepped in front of him smoothly. "Pilar, don't rush into a decision," he pleaded. "Remember that without the mirror, we never would have known you were in danger, and without the carpet, we never would have arrived in time to save you."

"That's true," Gabriel added. "The leaf *did* heal you, but it couldn't have worked without the other magic gifts. Are you sure you've made the right decision?"

"Indeed I am," Pilar said gently. She hugged Rafael and Gabriel, in gratitude for helping to save her life. "The leaf is not my favorite gift merely because it healed my illness," she explained. "It is my favorite because its giver could use its precious power only once, and he used it for me. The carpet can fly a million times. The mirror can show thousands of pictures. Miguel could have saved the leaf for himself; surely, he will need it someday when he is ill! But, no—by using it to heal me, it can never be used again." She held out her hand, and Miguel took it. "That is why I chose you," she told him. "Your gift showed that you love me even more than you love yourself."

The next time Pilar wore her wedding gown was the day she married Miguel. The king and queen beamed over their wise daughter and her loving husband. The people of the kingdom rejoiced over the happy couple. And even Rafael and Gabriel danced at their best friend's wedding feast, because their little brother had won the contest fair and square.

❦ 48 ❦

The Silk Bridegroom

A young woman sat in her favorite wicker chair, under her favorite palm tree, in the peaceful little courtyard of her home. On her lap she balanced a book, but she was not reading. Instead, she was anxiously watching her cup of coffee. Every few minutes a door inside the house would slam shut and the cup would tremble, spilling coffee into the delicate saucer. But right now all was quiet. Could *this* be the matchmaker who would finally find her a husband? No, she would not even hope.

"Too short!" "Too shabby!" "Too skinny!" Penina had heard her mother's voice dismiss every man in town the moment she saw the matchmakers' pictures.

Now, she heard a matchmaker speaking from inside the house. "Then tell me, madam, exactly what sort of man are you looking for?"

"I require only three things," her mother's voice answered coldly. "He must be as beautiful as my daughter, as smart as my husband, and as rich as me!"

Slam! Penina knew what that meant. The matchmaker had left in disgust, just as they always did.

Penina poked her head into her mother's office, blotting coffee stains from her book. "Mother, couldn't you try harder to work with the matchmakers?" she said. "What can you tell from pictures? Perhaps if we tried *talking* to some of the young men—"

"Why waste time, Penina?" her mother interrupted, not bothering to look up from her desk. "I've always judged people by how they look, and it's made me a rich woman. If people look rich, I charge them more. If people look poor, I refuse them a loan. Why should I change my ways now?"

Penina could not find fault with that logic. Yet she knew her mother was wrong. She had just opened her mouth to try a different argument when a servant appeared in the doorway and murmured, "Very old man here to see you, madam. Shabby clothes. Big sack on his back. Shall I send the beggar away?"

"Yes, yes, of course, and don't interrupt us again!" she answered impatiently.

"No, wait!" Penina said, leaning across the desk. "How do you *know* he's a beggar? What if he is a prince in disguise—or the prophet Elijah, for all you know?" She gave a hopeful laugh.

"All those books you read are giving you quite an imagination," her mother said with a matching chuckle. She pushed her papers away. "All right, Penina. If it will make you happy, let's invite the beg— I mean, the *gentleman* in."

The door opened wide. An old man slowly entered. He *is* a beggar, Penina thought with disappointment. But apart from his untidy hair and dusty boots, there was an air of amusement on his creased face. He looked at everyone piercingly, even the servant, who would not meet his gaze. Finally, he examined Penina's face and announced, "No problem! This one will be easy."

"*What* will be easy?" her mother demanded.

"Why, finding your daughter a husband, of course," answered the old man, setting his grimy sack on the elegant carpet. "Why else would a matchmaker come here?"

"*You*, a matchmaker?!" she stammered.

"Something told me you needed my kind of help," he said.

"You are right!" Penina said, clasping his hand and leading him away. "Mother, we won't disturb your work any longer."

Her mother stared at the empty doorway for a moment. Then she jumped up and shouted after them, "As beautiful as my daughter, as smart as my husband, and as rich as me! Those are my requirements!" But Penina and her visitor were already out of sight.

An hour later, it had all been decided: A banquet would be held the very next day. The finest young men of the region would be invited, and Penina herself would choose her husband from among them.

Upon hearing this plan, her mother's expression turned from doubtful to sour. "If we are doing all the work, then why do I need to pay a matchmaker?" she argued.

"Because if no one suits us, Mother, you will not have to pay him a penny," said her daughter. The matchmaker nodded cheerfully in agreement. Penina's mother opened her mouth. She closed it again. She frowned. Finally, she tossed out a scornful "Hmmmpph!" and went back to her work. And so it was settled.

The following day, the dining room was packed with young men—young men wearing golden rings and carrying jeweled walking sticks, young men discussing their businesses, young men examining the furniture greedily. Poor Penina frantically tried to get the matchmaker's attention, but he was busy trying to see above the heads of the crowd, as if he were expecting someone else.

Just as dessert was being served, a tall young man appeared in the dining room doorway. Hesitating, he pushed his round glasses higher onto the bridge of his nose and blushed at the sight of Penina. He was a student, she guessed, for his clothes were frayed at the cuffs and collar, and one shoulder was weighed down by a book bag. The servants took no notice, but the matchmaker rushed to offer him the seat right next to Penina.

Her mother, however, was having none of it. "Late and poor!" she roared at the matchmaker. "Is this the kind of husband you have in mind for my only daughter?" She yanked the student back to his feet by his thin jacket. "Out, all of you!"

Penina watched as her guests rushed out the door, and she knew that her chances of ever finding a husband were leaving with them. True, none of them had seemed very interesting, except for that tall student who had come in late.

Her eye wandered to the window, and she saw that same student standing across the street. He and the matchmaker were talking. The old man rummaged around in his sack. He needn't bother, Penina thought. There's nothing in that bag—nothing in the world!—that could make Mother accept a poor student as my husband.

But the moment Penina turned away, a knock sounded at the door, and she flew to open it. A tall man in a silk suit bowed low.

"Who is it, and what do you want?" came her mother's voice from her office.

"My name is Isaac, and I'm here for the banquet," said the young man, as he pressed his way inside.

"Why are you so late?" demanded Penina's mother, planting herself in the stranger's path. "The banquet is over." Then she took a long look at him. "Well, almost over," she added quickly.

"I'm so sorry," replied Isaac, handing his cape to one servant and his ivory walking stick to another, "but I was giving a lecture at the university and couldn't come

sooner." He grinned at Penina while adjusting his little round glasses. She smiled back, her face as rosy as his.

The matchmaker suddenly appeared, murmuring, "Beautiful, smart, and rich. Just what you ordered, I believe?" Penina's mother didn't answer. She had the dreamy air of someone planning a wedding and thinking about grandchildren.

On the day of Penina and Isaac's wedding, a crowd stood around the *chuppah*, waiting for the bride and groom to enter with their parents. The guests clapped excitedly, and joyful music rang out. Finally, Isaac's proud parents walked into the hall. And between them— What *were* they carrying? A silk suit and fancy scarf? An ivory walking stick?

The clapping stopped. The music stopped. The rabbi looked stern. Penina tried to hide a tiny smile. Her mother yelled, "What's the meaning of this?" The matchmaker stood at the edge of the crowd, apparently lost in thought.

Just then, Isaac walked in wearing his ragged student's clothes. He picked up the fancy scarf and gave it to Penina's mother. "When I came to your home dressed in my own clothes, you threw me out. But when I returned wearing these fine garments," he said, "you wanted me to marry your daughter. I thought it was my clothes, not me, that you wanted for a son-in-law. So here they are."

Penina was nodding in agreement. "He's right, Mother. The suit *is* beautiful, smart, and rich."

Penina's mother looked from her daughter to Isaac and back again. There was no doubt about it. Penina had got the best of her. Well, what was there to do? She kissed her daughter, hugged her soon-to-be son-in-law, and proclaimed, "Let the wedding begin!"

After the dancing, Penina's mother tried to find the matchmaker so that she could pay him his fee. But you can't go looking for Elijah. You have to wait until Elijah comes looking for you.

❧ 49 ❧

The Secret Ingredient

The Roman emperor Antoninus was well-known for his excellent government. He was well-known as a patron of the arts. He was well-known for his sense of justice. He was even well-known for his kind treatment of the Jews in his empire. What was little known about Antoninus was that he loved to eat.

If there were important financial problems to be discussed, the emperor had a choice. He could go to his treasurer, who was excellent with numbers. Or he could go to Elazar, the banker, whose wife was excellent with lamb stew. Which one do you think he chose? And that's how he governed his empire, loosening his belt a little with each passing day.

So it was not a coincidence that the emperor just happened to be passing by Rabbi Judah's house precisely at midday, when a strange and wonderful aroma danced through the air, as it did like clockwork every Saturday at noon. The emperor's carriage halted with a clatter outside the courtyard of the house, where he could already see a large table set with platters that made him gulp with anticipation. The rabbi's family streamed out to meet him.

"My dear friends, Judah and Adina," said the emperor, embracing his hosts as he climbed down. "I was on my way to the treasury, and I thought I would just drop by to ask your opinion on a very important matter. But, oh dear," he said, stopping abruptly when he reached the table, "I've come at an inconvenient time. You're just sitting down to lunch."

"Nonsense," said Rabbi Judah warmly. "You are always welcome."

"Oh, do join us," added his wife, Adina, as she sent their oldest daughter to fetch an extra chair and plate.

"But, Mother, isn't the treasury way over on the other side of—," the girl started to ask, before she remembered. "All right, I'll get another plate," she whispered instead, "but his chair is still out from last week's surprise visit. He's here so often he should just move his throne right in!"

Dish after fragrant dish stopped at the emperor's place, and nothing escaped his notice, from the carving of the meats to the spices in the chopped salad. Somewhere between the pickles and the olives, a loud burp escaped his lips as the emperor announced that he had forgotten the reason for his visit. But it didn't matter, because he was having such a fine time. Rabbi Judah brought out a lovely new wine for him to try. Every once in a while, the whole family would sing a song, or one of the little ones would stand on a chair to recite a passage learned at school that week. Adina passed some fruit turnovers with syrup spooned over the top for dessert, which reminded her of an amusing story about how her grandparents had met. After they'd all managed to stop laughing, the children drifted off to play, leaving the grown-ups to enjoy the perfect stillness of the afternoon. The scent of jasmine and gardenias engulfed the courtyard, and only the occasional trill of a bird could be heard. Emperor Antoninus happily, and a little sleepily, sat back in his chair to chew on a mint leaf, trying to delay his departure as long as he could.

Eventually, Rabbi Judah escorted his guest to the waiting carriage. "You're always welcome back whenever you remember what you wanted to discuss," he said, smiling and waving as the horses groaned and the carriage pulled away. The emperor smiled back and thoughtfully licked one finger all the way home.

The next day, his very first order of business was to gather his chefs, pastry masters, and cooking apprentices in the imperial kitchen. He described to them the exquisite meal he'd eaten the day before, down to the tiniest detail. They scurried off to the market to buy cumin, allspice, tamarind, even the honeyed syrup, and returned to prepare the same dinner he had enjoyed at the rabbi's house. Antoninus had shared so many of those Saturday meals that he knew every ingredient by heart, since Adina was proud of her cooking and willingly shared all the secrets of her kitchen. Now, exact copies of those very dishes would be waiting at his own table, cooked by his own chefs—every day, if he wished!

In fact, that's exactly what was waiting for Antoninus at dinnertime, and he eagerly sat down in front of a table that looked just like the lavish spread at the home of his friends. But he was sadly disappointed. As the imperial chefs hovered

watchfully nearby, he tasted dish after dish, stopping after only a few bites of each. They did *look* the same, exactly the same, but. . . .

Was it too soon to go back to Rabbi Judah's house?

Adina opened the door at once, looking a little confused to see the emperor in the middle of the week. "Your Majesty! What a wonderful surprise! Have you remembered the urgent business—"

"Yes, yes," said Antoninus distractedly as he strode into the little kitchen at the back of the house.

"What is it?" asked Rabbi Judah, following him with a worried face. "Is the empire in trouble? Has there been some disaster? Tell me, what worries you so? You can trust us."

Antoninus leaned against a stool and sighed. "No, no . . . it's just that . . . well, I hesitate to say this because you've been so kind to me with your many invitations." Then he leaned forward and spoke urgently. "I think you are keeping secrets from me! Everyone in my kitchen has been trying night and day to copy the meals you've been serving me, and they can't do it. When I ate the same food at your house, it was extraordinary!" He closed his eyes and could almost hear the clatter of cutlery and the giggles of the children. "I always leave your house each week with the most amazing sense of pleasure, of calmness. Is it a special spice, perhaps? Something ancient and exotic?" His voice rising, he stood up and exclaimed, "Whatever it is, I must have it. I don't care how much it costs, or how far I have to go to buy some. But you must tell me! *What is your secret ingredient?*"

Rabbi Judah patted his wife's hand and nodded at her. Finally, thought Antoninus, this riddle will be solved once and for all. I will find out their secret.

Adina grinned. "Emperor Antoninus, you know I would never keep a secret from such a dear friend. I do have a special ingredient, but I'm afraid that you cannot buy it in any market. I receive a new supply every week, though, and I will be happy to share it with you."

By now Antoninus was thoroughly confused and looked from Rabbi Judah to his wife and back. The two were smiling mysteriously at each other. Was this some kind of riddle?

Finally, Adina explained. "There is really nothing special about the food. What's special is the day," she told him. "On Shabbat, we stop all the work and all the worrying of the past week. We relax, pray, sing, eat, and spend time together. We feel at peace on Shabbat, and that's what makes our food so delicious."

✣ 50 ✣

Alef Wins

Before there were people, before there was a world, before there was a sun or a moon or stars, there were only words. The letters of the Hebrew alphabet were nothing but fiery jewels in God's crown, waiting to be released, waiting to come together, and waiting to shed light on the world.

God was ready to create the world and wondered aloud, "Where do I begin such an important project?"

Just then, the twenty-two letters of the alphabet burst from the crown and stood before God in a great commotion. All the letters were shouting at once, clamoring for attention. Pushing and shoving, each tried to speak first.

Tav, being broad and vigorous, pushed her way to the front. With both feet planted firmly, she boomed, "Use me, God. Create the world through me. I would make a great choice. Tav is for *Torah*, Your holy law. What better way to start the world than through me? Don't you agree?"

"Yes, Tav, you are special for being the letter to start the word *Torah*, but it would have been nicer not to brag about it," God said with a sigh. "To remind you not to be so impatient, you'll have to wait 3,036 years until I give the Torah to the Children of Israel on Mount Sinai." Tav slouched away quietly.

The other letters were busy arguing among themselves and boastfully making their cases before God. Gimel galloped about. Shin showed off by juggling his dot with all three arms. Yod flitted back and forth, telling anyone who would listen that she stood for the number ten, and so she should start the Ten Commandments, at the very least.

Meanwhile, Bet and his friend Alef were talking quietly in a corner, trying hard not to be noticed. Being the smallest, they usually tried to avoid the crowd and felt comfortable only in each other's company.

While everyone else was arguing, Alef was whispering earnestly into Bet's ear. "It should be you, you know. Go on, step forward. Speak to God. Why should they always get so much attention? You're special, too. Bet is for *b'rachah*, 'a blessing.' Every time someone blesses God, it will be thanks to you. Go on, Bet, tell God."

By this time, all the other letters had made their arguments to God. But each letter had been turned away, just as Tav had been.

In the quiet that followed, God heard what Alef had been saying.

"Tell God what?" God asked with an inviting smile.

"Uh-oh" was all Bet could manage to say.

"Don't be bashful, Bet. Alef is a good friend. What she said about you is true. On her recommendation, I will create the world through you. You will be the first letter of the first word in the Torah: Bet stands for *B'reishit*—'In the Beginning.' " The other letters, recognizing the justice of that decision, cheered.

"But," God added, "I will not forget the kindness and modesty of your friend, Alef."

Just then, Tav burst out, "Alef is the first letter, only number one! But I come last, the twenty-second letter! That's a lot more than one! Will you really put Alef before me?"

"Yes, I will," God replied. "In fact—little Alef, step forward. Come on, now, don't be shy." By then, the other letters were pushing Alef along to the front, congratulating her and patting her on the back.

Alef stood trembling before God's presence, blushing from head to toe.

"B-but God," she stammered, "I am worth only one. . . ."

"Oh, Alef, one is not small," God answered. "One is great. I, your God, am One. So here is *your* reward: I will begin the Ten Commandments with you: 'I, the Eternal One, am your God.' Alef is the first letter in *Anochi*, meaning 'I.' So the first thing the Children of Israel will see when they read the Ten Commandments is you."

Alef beamed as all the other letters rushed forward, picked her up, and carried her on their shoulders in a dance of celebration. Bet reached up on tiptoes and gave her a big hug.

Once again, this pure act of friendship did not go unnoticed, and they were rewarded even more. As Alef and Bet stood hugging, God announced that forevermore these friends would be united, and that, together, all the letters would be named in their honor.

And that is how the twenty-two letters came to be known as the *alef-bet*.

⚜ 51 ⚜

The Great Lights

I n the very beginning—when there was only light and darkness, heaven and earth—God created the sun and the moon.

"I have made you to be lights in heaven, to shine on the earth, and to divide day and night," God told them. "Any questions?"

Sun brightened and asked cheerfully, "When do I start?"

Before God could answer, Moon said, "With all due respect, God, why do you need *two* of us? Wouldn't I be enough? Look how brightly I can shine!" Moon puffed himself up as fat and round as he could and shot moonbeams out to every corner of the universe.

Sun was inflamed with anger. "How dare you try to outshine me! If God created me, it was for a good reason. So I'm staying, whether you like it or not!"

"But it's just too crowded up here!" Moon moaned. "We'll be bumping into each other all the time!"

"Quiet!" God finally said, sounding annoyed. "I need you *both*. Work it out yourselves, and then come back and tell me who will rule by day and who will rule by night."

Moon pulled Sun aside and whispered in her ear, "You know, I'm sorry I made a fuss. *You* go ahead and take the night. It will be much more relaxing and a lot less work, since everyone will be asleep." Moon smiled in a way he hoped was encouraging.

"Well, all right, I guess," Sun answered warily. "If it's okay with God, it's okay with me."

On the way back to tell God their decision, Moon could not stop thinking

about Sun and how bright she was. The more he thought about it, the more dissatisfied he became.

"Excuse me, Creator?" he said, approaching God. "I'm sorry to interrupt you. I see you're busy with some slimy things over there—"

"They're called reptiles," God said. "So, have you worked things out with Sun?"

"Yes, in fact, I agreed to rule by day, since Sun really wanted the night," Moon answered in a rush. "But I was thinking: If I rule by day, don't you think I should be brighter and bigger than Sun? After all, Your creatures will depend on me to shed light on their work. Wouldn't they sleep better, too, if Sun's light were, say, a little *dimmer*?"

But God, looking suspicious, turned away from the lizards and answered, "You are right, Moon. I can see that *one* of you needs to be cut down to size."

Suddenly, Moon felt his edges crumble and float away, trailing tiny sparks into the dark sky. With each spark of departing light, Moon became smaller and smaller. With each tear that Moon cried, he felt more and more ashamed of himself.

"Oh, God," Moon finally said, "I know why you made me smaller. I couldn't be happy with what you gave me. I even tried to trick Sun, my partner. I wanted more—I wanted everything! I was so wrong and foolish. That's why I'm smaller in Your eyes."

"I know you're sorry, sweet little Moon," God said gently. "Sun will rule by day, but you are special, too. People will be able to see you both in the daytime and at night. And you'll never be lonely, because your bits of light—let's call them stars—will keep you company. People will mark the calendar by you as you shrink and grow again every month. They will look for you with hope and wonder." Moon had stopped crying and was listening intently.

God gestured toward Sun, who was nearby, growing bigger and brighter with each moment. "Remember one more thing," God said. "In case either of you gets too proud again, I'm planning to send clouds to darken both your lights once in a while." God threw them a wink, Sun and Moon smiled sheepishly, and the great lights went their separate ways.

❧ 52 ❧

The Wooden Bowl

There once was a little old man named Elias, who had not always been so little or so old. As a young man, he had been strong and handsome. And when he had children of his own, his broad, square shoulders easily carried them to school every day. After a lifetime of hard work and much responsibility, though, his back bent, his shoulders rounded, and his skin wrinkled until at last he seemed half the size he once had been. His mind was still sharp though, his manner proud, and his clear blue eyes shone like beacons across a night sky.

A single glance from those eyes could tame his energetic grandson, Eli. "Grandpa," the little boy said as he climbed into his grandfather's lap one night, "tell me the story of this mark on your hand."

"When I was a young man," said his grandfather, "I was traveling from Aleppo through the desert, and I was stung by a scorpion." Elias saw the little boy's eyebrows knit with worry, even though he'd heard this story many times before. So the old man continued lightly, "A Bedouin sucked the venom out of my hand and saved my life! And I was left with this scar so that I can always remember that Bedouin and include him in my prayers. Because without him, there would be no me. And without me, there would be no you. And I'm so glad there is a you."

Eli snuggled in deeper, stroked his grandfather's hands again, and asked, "And what are these?"

"Those are my veins. You have them, too."

"But why are yours so big?"

"They carry blood to my heart, and I have a very big heart!"

"But Grandpa, I can see all your veins and bones. Your skin is so thin I can see right through it!"

"That's because I have nothing to hide. Now let's get you into bed for the night, and we'll talk more tomorrow."

Elias and Eli were always the first ones awake in the morning. Before anyone had even stirred, Elias was washed and dressed, his pants hiked up high on his belly, his face clean-shaven. He would make his own strong coffee and read the newspaper while Eli ate his breakfast and stared at him.

"Grandpa, why do you walk so slowly?" asked Eli on one of those mornings.

"Because I'm in no rush," Elias answered without moving the paper from in front of his face.

"Grandpa, why do you talk so loudly?"

"Because what I say is worth hearing."

"Grandpa, why do your hands shake?"

Elias lowered the paper and examined his hands. "Are they shaking? I must be excited to be with you." Then he picked up his paper again.

"Grandpa, don't forget—tonight's Shabbat! Our first since you moved in!"

Elias had not forgotten. He just wasn't looking forward to it. Elias and his son, Albert, loved each other, of course. But lately Albert had become so fussy! Elias knew that Albert cringed at his heavy Syrian accent and his loud laugh. Even at tonight's Shabbat table, something was sure to make him unhappy.

The scene was exactly as Elias had expected. The table was set with gold-rimmed china, delicate wineglasses sparkled atop an embroidered tablecloth, and a housekeeper rushed back and forth to make sure that everything was perfect. Elias sighed. It was a little too perfect for his taste. He was not used to being waited on.

When it was time for the *Kiddush*, he stood up and poured the wine himself. He knew, with only the briefest glance, that Albert was flinching over the few drops he'd spilled on the tablecloth—such worry over a silly piece of linen! But then Eli was raising his cup and asking, "Grandpa, aren't you going to sing the *Kiddush*?" so he said nothing.

After the blessings over the wine and challah, it was time for soup. Unfortunately, Elias dropped his spoon too heavily into the bowl, and it broke, sending a river of broth down the tablecloth and onto the carpet.

"Hoooo boy!" Elias hollered cheerfully as he dabbed at the table and his shirt.

"These *kibbe* are so fluffy they bounce right out of the bowl!"

"Good one, Grandpa!" Eli said, nudging him with an elbow while he rubbed at a greasy dribble on his chair cushion.

But Eli's father was not laughing. "Please try to be more careful, Father," Albert said evenly as he bent to mop up a tiny puddle on top of the old man's shoe.

"I'm sorry, my son," said Elias, trying to seem more serious. "I will try." He turned back to Eli. His blue eyes shone even bluer with the suppressed silliness.

The next day, Elias found that his place at the table was set differently from everyone else's. Instead of the usual fancy china, he had a wooden bowl, the kind of kitchen bowl used for mixing and chopping.

"What's this? Some kind of joke?" Elias asked, one eyebrow raised high.

But his son rarely joked. "Father, I thought it would be better not to worry about breaking things anymore, that's all," he answered, flashing Elias a quick look. "You don't mind, do you?"

"No, no, of course not. Not a bit. Why should I mind?" Elias answered. But his eyes dimmed as he stared at the table in front of him, while he ate very slowly and very carefully.

The next morning, when it was time for Eli to leave for Hebrew school, Albert went looking for his son.

"Eli!" he called. "Time to go! There's a special class about the holidays, so I don't want you to be late!" But the boy was not in the house or yard. Finally, Albert found him in the shed behind the house.

A block of wood was perched on the workbench in front of Eli, and woodworking tools were scattered around him. There were wood shavings on his pants and in his hair.

"What's all this mess?" Albert asked, as he brushed off the boy's clothes. "Eli, you'll be late for school!"

Eli did not look up as he spoke. "I'm almost done," he said. "I'm making a bowl."

"Bowl? What do you need a bowl for?" his father asked impatiently.

"*I* don't need it," said Eli.

There was a pause. Finally, Albert asked, "Then who's it for?"

"For you, Daddy, for when you get old," Eli said. "It will be yours when you're an old man, like Grandpa, and you come to live with me."

When Eli looked up, Albert's lips were pressed tightly together. For the first time, Eli noticed that his father's eyes were the same rich blue as his grandfather's—the same color, in fact, as his own.

Without speaking, Albert motioned for the boy to follow him into the house. He walked right past Eli's book bag, right past the garage. "Dad, why aren't you taking me to school?" Eli asked.

"But I *am* taking you to school," said his father in a quiet voice. "This morning, you will learn something about Yom Kippur," he added, as he knocked on the door to Elias's room.

Elias sat hunched in his easy chair, still in his pajamas, tilting his newspaper to catch the morning sunlight. He looked up in surprise as Albert entered. While Eli stood in the doorway, Albert knelt down gently in front of the old man and said, "Father, I've behaved terribly. I'm so sorry. Please forgive me."

Elias did not answer right away. When he bent forward, the sunshine reflected on his face, highlighting the silver in his hair and the light in his eyes. For a few moments, he stroked Albert's head, the way one might soothe a little child. He saw that Eli was watching the rhythm of his hands as he delicately pushed the strands from his son's forehead. And with each gentle stroke, Elias blessed the boy, too.

Story Notes

1. **The Angels Argue**: A Creation midrash based on Bialik (p. 13, nos. 46–49). Rosh HaShanah, in addition to marking the Jewish New Year, is traditionally celebrated as the world's birthday. Similar versions can be found in Ausubel, Bin Gorion, and Ginzburg.

2. **The Just-Right Prayer**: Adapted from "The Prayer of the Shepherd," a folktale found in Bin Gorion (vol. 3, p. 1259, no. 112). This tale reinforces Yom Kippur's emphasis on heartfelt prayer as preferable to rote ritual, no matter how magnificent.

3. **So What?**: Based on "What Does It Matter?" (Buber, bk. 1, p. 163). There are many arcane rules for building a sukkah, but the main themes of Sukkot remain charity, hospitality, and joy.

4. **The Bear Hug**: Based on "Conversion," (Buber, bk. 1, p. 200), this folktale is appropriate reading for Simchat Torah. What better way to celebrate the completion of the annual Torah cycle than to remember what a human story it is? Incidentally, teachers have always encouraged their students with sweets as they begin Torah study.

5. **Young Abraham**: One of the most well loved of midrashim. Adapted from Bialik (p. 31–33, nos. 5–8), with similar versions found in Ginzburg and Ausubel. Although he is referred to in this story as Abraham, the biblical patriarch was called Abram until the age of ninety-nine, when God changed his name preceding circumcision. We decided to use the more recognizable version so that young readers will understand that the child in this story and the Abraham commonly referred to are one and the same.

6. ***Mazal Tov!*** The trickster's name may vary, but Joha is a well-known stock character in Middle Eastern folktales. Our version is adapted from Bushnaq, "Djuha Borrows a Pot" (pp. 254–55).

7. **The Bag of Trouble**: Adapted from "The Pekl Story," retold by Helen Mintz (in Schram's *Chosen Tales*, p. 222). A shorter version, more a saying than a story, can be found in Buber ("The Choice," bk. 2, p. 73).

8. **One Day at a Time**: Most retellings of this folktale end with the motif of a sword that seems to become wood when an innocent person is to be executed. Our version is based on Noy's "Blessed Be God, Day by Day" (*Folktales of Israel*, p. 73); the hero's motto comes from Psalm 68:20.

9. **It's All for the Best**: Based on Bialik (pp. 230–31, no. 127); also found in Gaster (*Ma'aseh Book*), Bin Gorion, and Ginzburg. In folktales, the prophet Elijah often appears in disguise, sometimes as a beggar, to help the helpless.

10. **The Found Jewel**: Adapted from Isaacs ("A Four-Leaved Clover," no. 1, pp. 161–63). The theme of the imperious ruler taught a lesson by a humble, and sometimes simple, subject is a favorite of folktales worldwide.

11. **The Lost Bet**: A frequently retold talmudic legend from BT *Shabbat* 31a. Our version is adapted from Bialik (p. 205, no. 14).

12. **It's Not Fair!**: Adapted from Bin Gorion (vol. 2, pp. 644–46, no. 112). In other versions of this folktale, Elijah's companion is an adult, and the three misunderstood events reflect adult concerns. The tradition of Elijah's appearance at circumcision ceremonies is ancient.

13. **The Empty Fork**: This is an original story; the legend of the two angels is based on a talmudic legend from BT *Shabbat* 119b.

14. **The Priceless Stone**: Adapted from Bin Gorion ("Dama ben Netinah," vol. 2, p. 622, no. 84), this talmudic legend (BT *Kiddushin* 31a) is also found in Gaster (*Ma'aseh Book*). The Torah (Exodus 28) describes the High Priest's breastplate as containing twelve precious stones, each representing a different tribe. There is some debate about how to translate the names of the stones.

15. **The Ladle**: Adapted from Ausubel ("Asking for the Impossible," pp. 199–201), this fantasy tale features Rabbi Isaac Luria, the legendary mystic of Safed. He is sometimes referred to as the Holy Lion because *ari*, an acronym of his name, means lion in Hebrew.

16. **The Wobbly Table**: Adapted from Bialik (p. 214, no. 57). In other retellings of this story, the occupants of heaven are humans enjoying their reward after death; in our version, they are angels. Chanina ben Dosa, about whom there are many talmudic legends, is also featured in story 23.

17. **My Friend, the Sea Monster**: A little-known fantasy tale, adapted from Bialik (p. 771, no. 112).

18. **The Seeds of Honesty**: Adapted from Ausubel ("The Wise Rogue," p. 365); a similar version is found in Gaster (*Exempla of the Rabbis*, p. 169, no. 433). In most other versions, the thief is guilty. This folktale anticipates Tu BiSh'vat.

19. **The Bragging Contest**: Based on Torah (Judges 9:16; Psalm 92:13), Bialik (p. 11, no. 34; p. 28, nos. 127–28; pp. 62–63, nos. 28–31; p. 339, nos. 2, 38, 40; p. 340, nos. 43–44; p. 342, no. 59; p. 348, no. 112; p. 405, no. 25; p. 550, nos. 144–45; p. 551, no. 157; p. 586, nos. 110–12; p. 588, no. 130; p. 589, nos. 133–34, 136; p. 772, nos. 124–25, 128, 130; p. 773, nos. 133, 142), and Fahs ("The Trees Choose a King," pp. 45–47). Shimon bar Yochai, mentioned here, is featured in story 34.

20. **A Blessing Forever**: Based on Bialik (pp. 37–38, no. 36). This frequently retold parable illustrates God's promise to make Abraham the father of a great nation (Genesis 17).

21. **The Good-for-Nothing King**: Based on Rush, "Money Comes and Money Goes, But a Profession Lasts Forever" (pp. 224–26). In that retelling, the king's profession is carpet weaving.

22. **Joseph-the-Sabbath-Lover**: Adapted from Gaster, "Observance of Sabbath Rewarded" (*Ma'aseh Book*, pp. 8–9, no. 5). This popular talmudic tale can also be found in Bialik and Bin Gorion. Zohara's name means "splendor."

23. **What Happened to My Chickens?**: Based on Bialik (pp. 214–15, no. 59), but found in many collections. This is our second story featuring Chanina ben Dosa, the otherworldly scholar, and his long-suffering wife.

24. **The Royal Test**: Adapted from Noy, "Who Is a Hero? He Who Governs His Passions" (*Moroccan Folktales*, pp. 81–82) and based on a mishnah from *Pirkei Avot* 4:1. We substitut-

ed the familiar tune "Eliyahu HaNavi" for the Moroccan song in Noy's version, but the structure of the story is the same.

25. **Purim in Chelm**: An original story based on a suggestion by our friend Rabbi Melinda F. Panken. The antics of the lovable fools of Chelm, a mainstay of Jewish humor, are well-suited to the weeks before Purim. The reference to capturing the moon in a barrel is a fine illustration of Chelmite logic; a version of that story can be found in Simon (pp. 35–42).

26. **The Magic Donkey**: Adapted from Noy, "The Passover Miracle" (*Folktales of Israel*, pp. 179–80). This story features another poor but clever hero who is not averse to a bit of trickery. We've changed the setting to Purim.

27. **The Other Me**: Based on Ausubel ("The Columbus of Chelm," pp. 334–36). Our last Purim story is a classic tale of Chelm.

28. **Miriam Babysits**: An original midrash based on Exodus 2:1–10. Although the story of Baby Moses' rescue is very well known, we've decided to focus on Miriam as its young hero. The actions of women are central to the Passover story.

29. **Moses the Shepherd**: Based on Ausubel ("Moses the Shepherd," pp. 457–58), which draws on a midrash from *Sh'mot Rabbah*. This midrash illustrates the moment before God appears to Moses in the Burning Bush.

30. **The Perfect Seder**: Adapted from Rabinowicz ("The Man Who Slept through the Seder," pp. 211–14). A similar version comes from Buber ("The Seder of the Ignorant Man," bk. 1, p. 21). Folktales like these remind us that the minutiae of cleaning, cooking, and ritual observance pale in the face of a true celebration of the Exodus.

31. **Nachshon and the Sea**: Based on Bialik (pp. 72–73, no. 82). This last Passover story is based on a midrash (*M'chilta B'shalach* 5; BT *Sotah* 37a) on the often retold story of the splitting of the Red Sea.

32. **The New Moon**: Based on Torah (Exodus 32:1–35); *Midrash Rabbah* (Numbers 21:10); and Bialik (pp. 83–84, no. 57). Our version of this popular midrash focuses on the Israelite women's faith and on Miriam's leadership. This episode is the traditional basis for celebrating Rosh Chodesh as a women's holiday.

33. **The Spies**: Based on Torah (Exodus 3:17; Numbers 13:1–14:10; Deuteronomy 11:11) and Bialik (pp. 90–91, nos. 87–91; pp. 365–66, nos. 62, 67; p. 368, no. 84; p. 369, no. 92; pp. 370–71, nos. 101–4). This story celebrates Yom HaAtzma-ut, with twin emphases on the Land of Israel's beauty and the constant conflict that has surrounded its existence.

34. **Rabbi Shimon's Cave**: Adapted from Bialik (pp. 249–50, no. 221). The tradition of Lag BaOmer outings originates with students' visits to Shimon bar Yochai's hideout.

35. **The Crack in the Diamond**: Based on Ausubel, "The Blemish on the Diamond" (pp. 66–67). This folktale embraces two favorite themes: the foolish sovereign and the dangers of wanting life to be perfect.

36. **The Two Sisters**: Adapted from Bin Gorion ("A Story of the Temple," vol. 1, pp. 491–92). Our Yom Y'rushalayim story is based on the popular midrash linking the site of the Temple with love for others. The sisters' names mean "goodness" and "blessing" in Hebrew. Other versions have male protagonists.

37. **The Five-Shekel Thief**: Based on an anecdote written by Rabbi Zalmen Marozov (**www.torahfax.net**), and used here with his permission. This Shavuot story features holiday customs, but its message focuses on taking the Ten Commandments to heart.

38. **Dear God**: Adapted from Noy, "A Letter to the Almighty" (*Folktales of Israel*, pp. 85–87, no. 35) and Weinreich ("A Letter to God," pp. 163–66, no. 54). Our version retains the motif of

taking a figure of speech literally but omits the vindictive characters who try to thwart the hero.

39. **Deborah Lights the Way**: Based on Bialik (pp. 108–9, no. 20). This tale of one of our neglected foremothers highlights several profoundly Jewish themes: the centrality of learning, the interconnectedness of Torah and everyday life, and the recognition that actions speak louder than words.

40. **The Best Weapon**: Based on Torah (I Samuel 24:2–23). With its dangerous setting, an atmosphere of suspense, and the triumph of one man's conscience over violence, it's surprising that this story has been largely ignored.

41. **The King and the Worm**: Based on Torah (I Kings 5:9–10:29); Bialik (pp. 124–25, no. 111; pp. 126–27, no. 118); and Gaster (*Ma'aseh Book*, "Solomon and Ashmedai," pp. 183–90). Another legend about the humbling of an earthly sovereign. Most versions of this popular story include a powerful demon that Solomon must outwit.

42. **What the Baker Forgot**: An original story. Schram's "The Artist's Search" (*Jewish Stories*, pp. 259–62) also features a seeker finding his soul's desire at his own Shabbat table.

43. **Solomon and the Miser**: Adapted from Ausubel ("Hunger," pp. 136–38). We've added the detail of Solomon's knowing the language of birds.

44. **The Gift of Tears**: Based on Ausubel ("The First Tear," p. 452). The underlying theme of sadness and regret in this midrash anticipates Tishah B'Av.

45. **Rachel's Testimony**: Adapted from Bialik (pp. 146–48, no. 12). A unique midrash for Tishah B'Av.

46. **A Match Made in Heaven**: Adapted from Bin Gorion ("Solomon's Daughter," vol. 1, pp. 170–71, no. 83); similar versions can be found in Ginzburg and Isaacs. Retellings of this folktale are ubiquitous. Tu B'Av, the ancient holiday that celebrated finding one's true love, is making a modern-day comeback.

47. **The Wedding Present**: Adapted from Noy, "Who Cured the Princess?" (*Folktales of Israel*, pp. 139–42). A well-loved fantasy tale. In most stories, the youngest brother finds a magic apple. The motif of the magic leaf can be found in Schwartz's "The Mute Princess" (pp. 148–54). Incidentally, the brothers bear the names of angels.

48. **The Silk Bridegroom**: Adapted from Schram, "Welcome to Clothes" (*Tales of Elijah*, pp. 19–20) and Bushnaq ("Djuha's Sleeve," p. 257). We've added the prophet Elijah's role as a matchmaker.

49. **The Secret Ingredient**: Based on Bialik (p. 492, no. 65) and Gaster (*Ma'aseh Book*, "Why the Sabbath Meal Tastes So Good," pp. 8–9).

50. **Alef Wins**: Based on Ginzburg ("The Alphabet," vol. 1, pp. 5–8). At the time of year when Jews start preparing for the New Year, it seems appropriate to focus on this pre-Creation midrash, whose subject is humility.

51. **The Great Lights**: Based on Bialik (p. 11, nos. 36, 38). A legend explaining, in part, why the Jewish calendar runs on a lunar cycle.

52. **The Wooden Bowl**: Adapted from Schram, "Three Generations" (*Jewish Stories*, pp. 448–49). In a similar version by Gaster (*Exempla of the Rabbis*, p. 171, no. 437), the item given to the grandfather is a mantle, which the grandson cuts in half, reserving the other part for his own father. This story illustrates the themes of repentance, honoring parents, and the fundamental value of teaching children and learning from them.

Bibliography

Ausubel, Nathan. *A Treasury of Jewish Folklore*. New York: Crown Publishers, 1948.

Bialik, Hayim Nahman, and Yehoshua Hana Ravnitsky. *The Book of Legends*. Trans. William G. Braude. New York: Schocken Books, 1992.

Bin Gorion, Micha Joseph, coll., Emanuel Bin Gorion, ed., and I. M. Lask, trans. *Mimekor Yisrael*. 3 vols. Bloomington, Ind.: Indiana University Press, 1976.

Buber, Martin. *Tales of the Hasidim*. Bks. 1 and 2. New York: Schocken Books, 1991.

Bushnaq, Inea. *Arab Folktales*. New York: Pantheon Books, 1986.

Fahs, Sophia L. *From Long Ago and Many Lands*. Boston: Beacon Press, 1948.

Frankel, Ellen. *The Classic Tales: 4,000 Years of Jewish Lore*. Northvale, N.J.: Jason Aronson, 1989.

Gaster, Moses. *The Exempla of the Rabbis*. London-Leipzig: Asia Publishing, 1924.

_____. *The Ma'aseh Book of Jewish Tales and Legends*. 2 vols. Philadelphia: Jewish Publication Society, 1934.

Ginzburg, Louis. *The Legends of the Jews*. 7 vols. Philadelphia: Jewish Publication Society, 1909–1938.

The Holy Scriptures. Philadelphia: Jewish Publication Society, 1985.

Hyman, Naomi M. *Biblical Women in the Midrash: A Sourcebook*. Northvale, N.J.: Jason Aronson, 1997.

Isaacs, A. S. *Stories from the Rabbis*. New York: Charles L. Webster, 1893.

Noy, Dov. *Folktales of Israel*. Chicago: University of Chicago Press, 1961.

_____. *Moroccan Jewish Folktales*. New York: Herzl Press, 1966.

Plaut, W. Gunther, ed. *The Torah: A Modern Commentary*. New York: UAHC Press, 1981.

Rabinowicz, Tzvi. *The Prince Who Turned into a Rooster: One Hundred Tales from the Hasidic Tradition*. Northvale, N.J.: Jason Aronson, 1994.

Rush, Barbara. *The Book of Jewish Women's Tales*. Northvale, N.J.: Jason Aronson, 1994.

Schram, Peninnah. *Jewish Stories One Generation Tells Another*. Northvale, N.J.: Jason Aronson, 1987.

_____. *Tales of Elijah the Prophet*. Northvale, N.J.: Jason Aronson, 1991.

_____. *Chosen Tales*. Northvale, N.J.: Jason Aronson, 1995.

Schwartz, Howard. *Elijah's Violin & Other Jewish Fairy Tales*. New York: Harper & Row, 1983.

Simon, Solomon. *The Wise Men of Chelm*. New York: Behrman House, 1961.

Soncino Midrash Rabbah. Judaic Classics Libraries. Soncino Press, 1991–5. CD-ROM.

Weinreich, Beatrice Silverman. *Yiddish Folktales*. Trans. Leonard Wolf. New York: Pantheon Books, Random House, 1988.

Topic Index